Anxiety and Stress

Series Editor: Cara Acred

Volume 279

Independence Educational Publishers

WITHDRAWN

First published by Independence Educational Publishers

The Studio, High Green

Great Shelford

Cambridge CB22 5EG

England

© Independence 2015

Copyright

Photocopy licence

British Library Cataloguing in Publication Data

Anxiety and stress. -- (Issues ; 279)
1. Stress (Psychology) 2. Stress management.
I. Series II. Acred, Cara editor.
155.9'042-dc23

ISBN-13: 9781861687074

Printed in Great Britain

Zenith Print Group

Contents

Introduction

Anxiety and Stress is Volume 279 in the **ISSUES** series. The aim of the series is to offer current, diverse information about important issues in our world, from a UK perspective.

ABOUT ANXIETY AND STRESS

Today, 20% of people say that they regularly feel anxious and a further 20% take time off work due to stress. This book explores the impacts of stress and anxiety, alongside symptoms and coping strategies. It also considers the stigma surrounding stress in the workplace and examines the implications and causes of post-traumatic stress disorder.

OUR SOURCES

Titles in the **ISSUES** series are designed to function as educational resource books, providing a balanced overview of a specific subject.

The information in our books is comprised of facts, articles and opinions from many different sources, including:

⇨ Newspaper reports and opinion pieces

⇨ Website factsheets

⇨ Magazine and journal articles

⇨ Statistics and surveys

⇨ Government reports

⇨ Literature from special interest groups

A NOTE ON CRITICAL EVALUATION

Because the information reprinted here is from a number of different sources, readers should bear in mind the origin of the text and whether the source is likely to have a particular bias when presenting information (or when conducting their research). It is hoped that, as you read about the many aspects of the issues explored in this book, you will critically evaluate the information presented.

It is important that you decide whether you are being presented with facts or opinions. Does the writer give a biased or unbiased report? If an opinion is being expressed, do you agree with the writer? Is there potential bias to the 'facts' or statistics behind an article?

ASSIGNMENTS

In the back of this book, you will find a selection of assignments designed to help you engage with the articles you have been reading and to explore your own opinions. Some tasks will take longer than others and there is a mixture of design, writing and research-based activities that you can complete alone or in a group.

FURTHER RESEARCH

At the end of each article we have listed its source and a website that you can visit if you would like to conduct your own research. Please remember to critically evaluate any sources that you consult and consider whether the information you are viewing is accurate and unbiased.

Useful weblinks

www.anxietyuk.org.uk

www.axappphealthcare.co.uk

www.bacp.co.uk

www.bma.org.uk

www.bupa.co.uk

www.careuk.com

www.employeebenefits.co.uk

www.helpguide.org

www.hscic.gov.uk

www.hse.gov.uk

www.mind.org.uk

news.liv.ac.uk

news.stanford.edu

www.nhs.uk

www.nightline.ac.uk

www.nopanic.org.uk

www.patient.co.uk/health/anxiety

www.parentdish.co.uk

www.time-to-change.org.uk

Stress

Stress is how you feel when the pressure you're under exceeds your ability to cope. Everyone reacts to stress differently. It can depend on your personality and how you respond to pressure.

Symptoms of stress

Everyone reacts to stress in different ways. However, there are some common symptoms to look out for. Your symptoms can be psychological, emotional, behavioural or physical, or a mix of these.

Psychological symptoms of stress can include:

⇨ constant worrying

⇨ an inability to concentrate

⇨ feeling that you have poor judgement

⇨ seeing only the negative

⇨ anxious thoughts

⇨ memory problems.

If you're affected emotionally by stress, your symptoms may include:

⇨ mood swings or changes in your mood

⇨ irritability or having a short temper

⇨ an inability to relax

⇨ feeling overwhelmed

⇨ a sense of loneliness

⇨ depression

⇨ low self-esteem.

Your behaviour might also change and you may be:

⇨ eating more or less than usual

⇨ sleeping too much or too little

⇨ isolating yourself from others

⇨ neglecting or putting off responsibilities

⇨ using alcohol, tobacco or illegal drugs to relax

⇨ developing nervous habits; for example, nail biting or not being able to sit still.

Stress can affect you physically, causing symptoms such as:

⇨ aches and pains

⇨ diarrhoea and constipation

⇨ nausea or dizziness

⇨ chest pains

⇨ loss of sex drive.

These symptoms may be caused by problems other than stress. If you have any of them, speak to your GP for advice.

If you have a pre-existing health condition, stress may cause it to worsen or flare-up. For example, conditions such as migraine, eczema, asthma, irritable bowel syndrome or psoriasis can all be aggravated by stress.

Diagnosis of stress

There is no specific test to diagnose stress. If you think you're stressed or if you feel very anxious, talk to those around you who are likely to be supportive, or your GP. Your GP will usually be able to recognise the symptoms and give you advice about how to deal with it. Your GP may also suggest that you talk to a counsellor.

You might feel reluctant to ask for help if you're stressed or feel under pressure. But don't be afraid to speak to your GP, friends or family. It's important to recognise the symptoms of stress so you can learn how to manage them and begin to feel better.

One way of helping to identify your stress triggers, how you react to them and how they make you feel, is to keep a diary. You could make a note of what made you stressed, how stressed you became, what symptoms you experienced and how well you coped.

Treatment options for stress

There are a number of treatment options for stress. These are described below. Which treatments you are offered will depend on your personal circumstances. Your GP will discuss these with you to help you make a decision that's right for you. Your decision will be based on your GP's expert opinion and your own personal values and preferences.

To be able to tackle stress, it's important to recognise the symptoms as well as the problems that it's causing. There are a number of ways to reduce the effect that stress can have on you. If these don't work, your GP may recommend other options, such as cognitive behavioural therapy (CBT).

Self-help

Exercise can be effective at relieving stress and is good for your wellbeing. It can improve your mood, give you a sense of achievement and help you release tension. According to the Department of Health, there's evidence that physical activity reduces your risk of depression and improves your quality of sleep. It helps reduce stress hormones and stimulates the release of endorphins (the hormones that make you feel good).

It can help to incorporate exercise into your daily routine. A brisk walk to the shops, cycling to work or gardening can help. The recommended healthy level of physical activity is 150 minutes (two-and-a-half-hours) of moderate exercise per week. One way to achieve this is to do 30 minutes of exercise at least five days a week.

There are a number of other things you can try to help deal with and manage your stress better.

⇨ Manage your time more effectively and prioritise more important jobs first.

⇨ Adopt a healthy lifestyle – eat a balanced diet, rich in fruit and vegetables, exercise regularly, and make sure you get enough sleep.

⇨ Know your limits – don't take on too much.

⇨ Find out what causes you to feel stressed and try to change your thoughts and behaviour to reduce it – talking things over with a friend or a family member can help.

⇨ Try not to get into situations that make you feel angry or upset.

⇨ Accept the things you can't change and concentrate on the things you have control over.

⇨ Make time for the activities you enjoy and for the things that make you feel relaxed – you're more likely to neglect this area of your life if you're stressed.

⇨ Find time to meet friends and have fun – arrange to do something you enjoy.

⇨ Develop a positive thinking style – try to look at a problem differently or discuss it with someone.

⇨ Don't drink too much alcohol, or caffeine, or use tobacco or illegal drugs as a way to cope. In the long term, these things will only make you feel worse.

You can also learn techniques to manage your stress from self-help books, podcasts and CDs. Or by attending a stress management course. Some people find that meditative approaches, such as mindfulness, meditation, yoga or tai chi, are effective at reducing stress and anxiety. Yoga and tai chi help you control your breathing and relax your mind. Meditation helps you learn to reduce anxious thoughts and become calmer.

Explore the options available and find a solution that fits you, your lifestyle, work and personality. There is no right or wrong approach as everyone reacts to stress in different ways. And different approaches will work for different people.

Talking therapies

CBT is a talking treatment. It looks at how situations can lead to

thoughts that impact your feelings and behaviour. It aims to change the way you think and behave, and helps you to challenge negative thoughts or feelings.

CBT can help to treat many problems, such as sleeping difficulties, relationship problems, drug and alcohol abuse, anxiety or depression. The therapy focuses on your thoughts, images, beliefs, feelings and attitudes (known as your cognitive processes) and how these relate to the way you behave. CBT sessions may be on a one-to-one basis or with a group of people. Sessions may last for between five and 20 weeks, with each session typically lasting between 30 and 60 minutes.

Medicines

Medicines are not generally helpful for treating stress.

Complementary therapies

Some people find that complementary therapies, including acupuncture, visualisation, reflexology and herbal remedies, offer some benefit. However, there isn't enough evidence to say if they are effective or not.

Massage and aromatherapy can promote a sense of wellbeing and provide a relaxing environment that helps you unwind. There's little scientific evidence to show whether or not aromatherapy is an effective treatment for stress.

You may find herbal remedies helpful, but it's important to remember that natural doesn't mean harmless. Herbal remedies contain active ingredients and may interact with other medicines or cause side-effects. Don't start taking any herbal remedies without speaking to your pharmacist first.

⇨ The above information is reprinted with kind permission from BUPA. Please visit www.bupa.co.uk for further information.

Stress-related and psychological disorders in Great Britain 2014

Work-related stress depression and anxiety is defined as a harmful reaction people have to undue pressures and demands placed on them at work.

The latest estimates from the Labour Force Survey (LFS) show:

⇨ The total number of cases of work-related stress, depression or anxiety in 2013/14 was 487,000 (39%) out of a total of 1,241,000 cases for all work-related illnesses.

⇨ The number of new cases of work-related stress, depression or anxiety in 2013/14 was 244,000.

⇨ The rates of work-related stress, depression or anxiety, for both total and new cases, have remained broadly flat for more than a decade.

⇨ The total number of working days lost due to stress, depression or anxiety was 11.3 million in 2013/14, an average of 23 days per case of stress, depression or anxiety.

⇨ The industries that reported the highest rates of total cases of work-related stress, depression or anxiety (three-year average) were human health and social work, education and public administration and defence.

⇨ The occupations that reported the highest rates of total cases of work-related stress, depression or anxiety (three-year average) were health professionals (in particular nurses), teaching and educational professionals, and health and social care associate professionals (in particular welfare and housing associate professionals).

The THOR-GP reporting network did not suggest any significant changes in the reported incidence of work-related mental ill health in the most recent three years (2011–2013) where a consistent method for reporting has been used.

General practitioners in the THOR-GP reporting scheme identify workloads, changes at work and interpersonal relationships as the main events leading to the work-related stress depression and anxiety health cases seen in their clinics.

2013/2014

⇨ The above information is reprinted with kind permission from Health and Safety Executive. Please visit www.hse.gov.uk for further information.

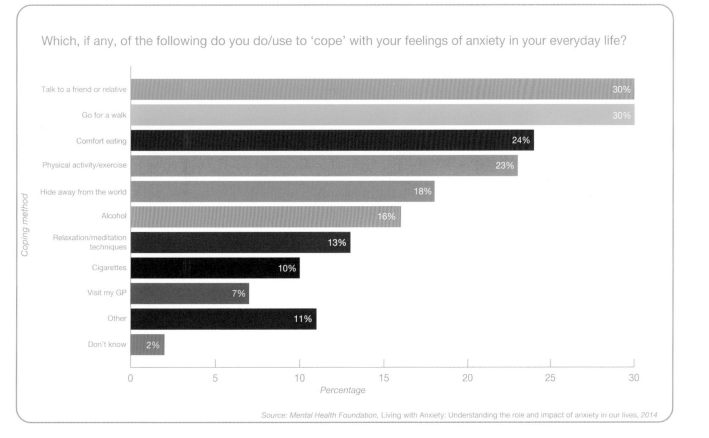

Which, if any, of the following do you do/use to 'cope' with your feelings of anxiety in your everyday life?

Coping method	Percentage
Talk to a friend or relative	30%
Go for a walk	30%
Comfort eating	24%
Physical activity/exercise	23%
Hide away from the world	18%
Alcohol	16%
Relaxation/meditation techniques	13%
Cigarettes	10%
Visit my GP	7%
Other	11%
Don't know	2%

Source: Mental Health Foundation, Living with Anxiety: Understanding the role and impact of anxiety in our lives, 2014

What is post-traumatic stress disorder?

If you are involved in or witness a traumatic event, it is common to experience upsetting, distressing or confusing feelings afterwards. The feelings of distress may not emerge straight away – you may just feel emotionally numb at first. After a while you may develop emotional and physical reactions, such as feeling easily upset or not being able to sleep.

This is understandable, and many people find that these symptoms disappear in a relatively short period of time. But if your problems last for longer than a month, or are very extreme, you may be given a diagnosis of post-traumatic stress disorder (PTSD).

There's no time limit on distress, and some people may not develop post-traumatic symptoms until many years after the event. Additionally, not everyone who has experienced a traumatic event develops PTSD.

Other terms for PTSD

The diagnosis 'PTSD' was first used by veterans of the Vietnam War, but the problem has existed for a lot longer and has had a variety of names, including:

⇨ shell shock

⇨ soldier's heart

⇨ battle fatigue

⇨ combat stress

⇨ post-traumatic stress syndrome (PTSS).

Today, the term PTSD can be used to describe the psychological problems resulting from any traumatic event.

'I was emotionally numb, kept people distant and was prone to drastic loss of self-control and anger'

What are the symptoms?

The symptoms of PTSD can vary from person to person, although you may experience some of the following.

Reliving aspects of the trauma:

⇨ vivid flashbacks (feeling that the trauma is happening all over again)

⇨ intrusive thoughts and images

⇨ nightmares

⇨ intense distress at real or symbolic reminders of the trauma

⇨ physical sensations, such as pain, sweating, nausea or trembling.

Alertness or feeling on edge:

⇨ panicking when reminded of the trauma

⇨ being easily upset or angry

⇨ extreme alertness

⇨ a lack of or disturbed sleep

⇨ irritability and aggressive behaviour

⇨ lack of concentration

⇨ being easily startled

⇨ self-destructive behaviour or recklessness.

Avoiding feelings or memories:

⇨ keeping busy

⇨ avoiding situations that remind you of the trauma

⇨ repressing memories (being unable to remember aspects of the event)

⇨ feeling detached, cut off and emotionally numb

⇨ being unable to express affection

⇨ using alcohol or drugs to avoid memories.

You may also develop other mental health problems, such as:

⇨ severe anxiety

⇨ a phobia

⇨ depression

⇨ a dissociative disorder

⇨ suicidal feelings.

What causes PTSD?

The situations we find traumatic can vary from person to person and different events can lead to PTSD. It may be that your responses have been bottled up for a long time after the traumatic event has passed. Your problems may only emerge months or sometimes years after a traumatic experience, affecting your ability to lead your life as you'd like to.

A traumatic event could include:

⇨ a serious accident, for example a car crash

⇨ an event where you fear for your life

⇨ being physically assaulted

⇨ being raped or sexually assaulted

⇨ abuse in childhood

⇨ a traumatic childbirth, either as a mother or a partner witnessing a traumatic birth

⇨ extreme violence or war

- ⇨ military combat

- ⇨ seeing people hurt or killed

- ⇨ a natural disaster, such as flooding or an earthquake

- ⇨ losing someone close to you in disturbing circumstances.

The following factors may also make you more vulnerable to developing PTSD after experiencing a traumatic event, or might make the problems you experience more severe:

- ⇨ experiencing repeated trauma

- ⇨ getting physically hurt or feeling pain

- ⇨ having little or no support from friends, family or professionals

- ⇨ dealing with extra stress at the same time, such as bereavement or loss

- ⇨ previously experiencing anxiety or depression.

Anyone can experience a traumatic event, but you may be more likely to have experienced one if you:

- ⇨ work in a high-risk occupation, such as the police or military

- ⇨ are a refugee or asylum seeker

- ⇨ have suffered childhood abuse.

Different types of trauma can have different types of impact. If you experienced trauma at an early age or if the trauma went on for a long time then you may be diagnosed with 'complex PTSD'. Treating 'complex PTSD' usually requires more long-term, intensive help than supporting you to recover from a one-off traumatic event.

How can I help myself?

After a traumatic event you may feel numb, dazed and disorientated. Many people find it hard to accept what has happened to them and you may behave as though nothing bad has happened. This response may allow you time away from the trauma and you may subconsciously be beginning to process what you've been through. When you feel ready, you may find the following ideas helpful.

Talk to someone close to you

Talking about your feelings, when you feel ready, may be a good way of coming to terms with the experience. You may turn to friends, relatives and colleagues, or seek professional help when you decide you do want to talk about what you've been through.

Talk to people with similar experiences

It may be very helpful for you to share your experiences with others who have been through something similar. This can be an extremely important step in moving away from isolation and towards regaining control of your life. Organisations such as First Person Plural can support you if you experience a dissociative condition as a result of abuse in childhood.

PANDAS can support you if you have experienced birth trauma and their website provides details of local support groups you can join.

'I was emotionally numb, kept people distant and was prone to drastic loss of self-control and anger'

Give yourself time

Everyone will have their own unique responses, and will need to proceed at their own pace. Talking before you want to might not be helpful. It may make you relive memories of the event, increasing the risk of flashbacks or nightmares. Allow yourself to feel ready to talk about your experiences.

Mindfulness

Mindfulness is a technique for becoming more aware of the present moment. It can help us enjoy the world around us more, and understand ourselves better. Some of the ways you could practise mindfulness are through meditation, tai chi or yoga. Some people find this helps them manage anxiety and stress. Be Mindful has more information.

Contact an organisation for support

You may find it useful to contact an organisation that specialises in PTSD, such as ASSIST trauma care. They will be able to give you advice, information and support. You may find it particularly useful to find a specialist organisation with expertise in the particular type of trauma you have experienced. For example, Combat Stress offers support for British Armed Forces Veterans who have mental health problems. Lifecentre offers support for anyone who has experienced sexual abuse. Freedom from Torture offers support for people who have been tortured or who are refugees.

Visit your GP

If you want to, you can ask your GP for help and discuss the support options with them. Before prescribing treatment for PTSD, your GP or mental health specialist will do an assessment so that they can match the treatment to your specific needs.

Doctors and therapists should be aware of your cultural and ethnic background. If you need an interpreter, they should arrange this for you.

They should also assess the impact of the traumatic event on all your close family and provide appropriate support.

⇨ The above information is reprinted with kind permission from Mind. Please visit www.mind.org.uk for further information.

© Mind 2015

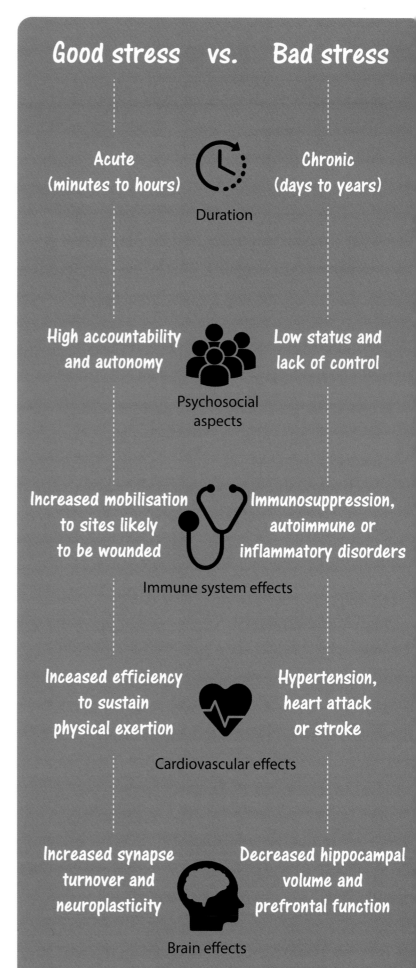

Source: What, me worry? By Kristin Sainani, Stanford.edu

Spotting the sources of stress

By Vivienne Nathanson

When I was a senior trainee and was asked to work with a recently qualified doctor who had multiple sclerosis, I was happy to make adjustments. Although she couldn't run to cardiac arrest, there were other things she can do where her physical abilities wouldn't matter so much.

Unfortunately, when doctors have mental health problems they may find their workplaces are less willing to make adjustments.

Medicine is a high-stress profession and doctors often expect a lot of themselves. They can't always get it right and this fundamental conflict in trying to cope can cause them to become depressed or substance dependent.

I think almost any doctor would say they are aware of colleagues who have problems. Although the issues may not be so severe that they need to stop work, their health is still significantly affected and their practice may be put at risk.

The International Conference on Physician Health at BMA House starting on Monday will present doctors with the evidence about how to spot stress early, how to reduce stress and how to treat it. This may help avoid people getting into the vicious circle of needing help and not getting it.

This year's theme, 'Milestones and Transitions – Maintaining the Balance' will look at the risk factors, prevention strategies, treatment strategies, secondary prevention and make sure research findings are known and well supported.

Doctors have more problems at times of transitions such as changing career speciality or grade. They may not have built their support structures for these working issues and take on different responsibilities.

Transitions can also be associated with other stresses such as moving house or getting married which tend to happen around the same time. For example if you're a medical student in University of Liverpool and you get your first house job in Lancaster and have to move, this becomes an extra stressor on top of the clinical job.

Doctors need to be able to admit they aren't completely sure of what they're meant to do. The difference between being the most senior trainee and being the consultant is that you don't have someone to check with that you're making the right decision. People become quite aware of that.

Junior doctors often tell us early on in their career that they find great difficulty in balancing demands. They may have new patients coming in and existing patients on the ward but with consultants or more senior juniors dashing off to clinics they're not sure who to ask for help.

It may not just be about clinical matters, but about things like how to talk to a patient's family to tell them there's not much more they can do or balancing the time on the wards.

Time management may have significant clinical consequences for the patient. Doctors can feel very lonely and exposed and don't necessarily have the confidence to tell anyone. We have to create an environment which is conducive to asking questions.

One of the highlights of this year's conference will be the use of acted scenarios to explore transitions in professional and personal life. We hope this will get people talking not just at the event, but when they're having coffee later. They can talk through how they would handle similar situations and if they have had similar cases.

The conference is not just about theory, it's about practical example. We hope to make things better for the next case or prevent the next case from actually happening.

15 September 2014

⇨ The above information is reprinted with kind permission from BMA. Please visit www.bma.org.uk for further information.

Is stress contagious?

Exams looming, a large unexpected bill, tension at work? These don't have to be your problems for your health to be affected by them.

We all know what it's like to feel stressed because of our relationship, money or work worries. But many of us also have to deal with the impact of stress on those close to us. And this second-hand stress can have a dramatic effect on our lives.

Are you susceptible?

Psychology Professor Elaine Hatfield of the University of Hawaii, and others, have carried out research in this area and developed the theory that, along with other feelings and emotions, stress is contagious – something we can catch from those around us.

Elaine explained there is an Emotional Contagion Scale – a set of 15 statements to measure susceptibility to 'catching' other peoples' emotions. For instance, if you answer 'always', to the statement 'I tense when overhearing an angry quarrel' you're likely to be more susceptible to emotional contagion than someone who answers 'never'.

Synchronised emotions

Researchers believe emotional contagion can happen when we imitate people's facial expressions, vocal sounds, language and posture, often without realising it. For example, if someone smiles at you, often you smile back, and may feel happier because of this.

As a result of this mimicry we are more likely to synchronise with other people, and pick up on their feelings. The good news is that emotional contagion applies to more positive feelings as well, such as happiness.

Consequences of stress

Experts in this field believe emotional contagion affects groups as well as individuals. Some believe it could be behind reports of mass hysteria.

But is the theory that we can 'catch' stress from others, as easily as a cold, generally accepted?

'We can't talk about stress in the same sense as a physical illness or disease,' says Dr Martin Bamber, Consultant Clinical Psychologist and founder of the York CBT Centre.

'However, when someone is stressed emotionally, they might be more irritable and short-tempered, perhaps feeling unwell and taking time off sick. And that can have consequences for those around them. Other people will be on the receiving end of the consequences of stress.'

The expert's opinion

'I think there is truth in this idea to a degree,' says Dr Nick Kambitsis of psychology consultancy Nicholson McBride. 'It depends on how the stress manifests itself in the individual.'

'If they become snappy and irritable, don't listen and don't engage with other people, I agree it can be contagious, because it will have an impact on people around them. But not everyone responds to stress in this way. Some withdraw, and some stay calm and consistent.'

Stress and your health

Stress, at the right time and place, can be useful. A sudden surge of hormones when you need it can make the difference between catching the bus or missing it – or winning the match or losing.

However, long-term stress – when you're under more pressure than you can cope with – can take its toll on your health. And that's a good reason to avoid stress if you can.

Symptoms such as headaches, trouble sleeping and being unable to concentrate can be a result of stress. Other, longer-term problems include blood sugar imbalance, increased abdominal fat and high blood pressure. These can lead to serious health problems, such as heart disease and stroke.

Side-step your second-hand stress

Expert opinion points towards a knock-on effect of spending time with someone who is stressed. But you can take steps to reduce the effect their problems have on you.

⇨ Exercise. Exercise can be a good way to relieve stress. This is because it helps use up the hormones the body produces when under stress. It relaxes muscles, strengthens the heart, improves blood circulation and releases endorphins (chemicals that give a sense of wellbeing).

⇨ Use your brain and relax. Using your brain in a different way can help relieve stress. Listen to music, cook, read a favourite book – do something you enjoy and find relaxing.

⇨ Talk about it. Taking a more direct approach with the person causing your stress can help. 'Have a conversation with the family member or work colleague. Talk about the problem, and acknowledge that it exists,' says Dr Kambitsis.

'Often you can come up with strategies to deal with the problem. You may look at the past, and how they – and you – dealt with similar situations. Ask what you as a family or work team can do about the problem, what's going to make them feel better.' It should make you feel better too.

For more information on managing stress why not visit our Stress Centre where you will find features on 'stress proofing techniques', 'managing pressure' and 'helping your child beat stress'.

⇨ The above information is reprinted with kind permission from AXA PPP Healthcare. Please visit www. axappphealthcare.co.uk for further information.

Dwelling on negative events biggest cause of stress

A study by psychologists at the University of Liverpool has found that traumatic life events are the biggest cause of anxiety and depression, but how a person thinks about these events determines the level of stress they experience.

Researchers from the University's Institute of Psychology, Health and Society analysed the responses of over 32,000 participants, aged 18–85 years, who completed the BBC's 'Stress Test', an online survey to explore the causes and consequences of stress.

'Thinking style' as much a factor

The study – the biggest of its kind in the UK – found that traumatic life events were the single biggest determinant of anxiety and depression followed by a family history of mental illness and income and education levels. Relationship status and social factors made smaller – but still significant – contributions to stress. However, the results revealed that a person's thinking style was as much a factor in the level of anxiety and depression a person experienced.

The 'Stress Test', which was launched on BBC Radio 4's All in *The Mind* and available on the BBC website to complete, asked participants a range of questions about their family history of mental health problems, life events, income and education levels, relationship status and social circumstances.

It also asked participants about how they responded to stressful situations; for example, did they talk to friends about their problems, did they turn to alcohol to reduce stress, did they blame themselves.

Professor Peter Kinderman, Head of the Institute of Psychology, Health and Society, led the research. He said: 'Depression and anxiety are not simple conditions and there is no single cause. We wanted to find out more about what caused people to suffer from anxiety and depression and why some people suffered more than others.

'Whilst we know that a person's genetics and life circumstances contribute to mental health problems, the results from this study showed that traumatic life events are the main reason people suffer from anxiety and depression. However, the way a person thinks about, and deals with, stressful events is as much an indicator of the level of stress and anxiety they feel.'

Leading cause of disability

'Whilst we can't change a person's family history or their life experiences, it is possible to help a person to change the way they think and to teach them positive coping strategies that can mitigate and reduce stress levels.'

Mental health problems affect one person in every four, making it the leading cause of disability. Its direct cost to England alone is estimated at £41.8 billion per annum but the wider costs in terms of the economy, benefits, lost productivity at work, amounts to more than £70 billion per year.

The research, in collaboration with the Universities of Manchester and Edinburgh, is published in PLUS One.

17 October 2013

⇨ The above information is reprinted with kind permission from the University of Liverpool and Professor Peter Kinderman, Head of the Institute of Psychology, Health and Society. Please visit news.liv.ac.uk for further information.

Stress and mental illness: talking about the 'glass ceiling for men'

From _steve-'s blog.

We all know stress. Most of us have experienced a growing sense of panic for instance when having too much to do all at one time, while deep down we either want to shout in fury or run away.

A real, almost physical change to the body, a chemical rearranging of hormones, transmitters, biochemical connections…

Stress can be the driver behind psychic change. It can have an effect over time like being caught in a fractured relationship, or trapped in a high-pressured job you don't enjoy.

To admit stress is taken as a sign of weakness – this is particularly true for men

When I've spoken to managers and directors, in workshops on health and safety and stress, about carrying out organisation-wide stress surveys they've consistently said that they would never want to admit to 'stress'. Especially middle managers, those who are trying to rise to positions of greater responsibility. To admit to stress is taken as a sign of weakness, an inability to cope, and I think this is particularly true for men.

As I mentioned in my last blog, I am still trying to decide when or whether, at work, to confess to my personal experience of mental ill health problems because of the sense of weakness and the possibility of a glass ceiling for men in their career progression. However, when I first 'came out' about my breakdowns and my illness, in the health and safety press, I had emails from a variety of people both men and women who were all grateful for me 'speaking' up, particularly in the world of work.

Stress is a result of each individual's life experience and is usually very real

I had seven years of psychotherapy on and off (but mostly on!) and it's true that after a breakdown, you may become more resilient to pressure and stress, more able to manage your reactions.

Some people think that stress is all in the imagination or that you are 'putting it on' to get time off work…however, stress is a result of each individual's life experience, their upbringing, their relationships, the associations and memories they have, and the situation they find themselves in…and it is usually very real.

Often men laugh it off, almost as if it is effeminate, it is a put down like the bully who does not respect the individual. And ironically, I can do the same to myself, I can choose to ignore the warning signs and to dismiss my reactions without truly listening to what lies beneath…

Creativity and mindfulness can help us to cope with stress

Stress can of course arise for a whole host of reasons. A friend of mine used to name these reasons on the fingers of one hand: family, friends, finance, relationships, work, and in the centre of the palm: health.

Most of us can cope with brief periods of overload but when worries become prolonged and chronic, the stress that they give rise to can start to eat away at the balance of the psyche and upset the body's equilibrium creating ill health, both physical and mental. This can show up as time off work, stomach ulcers, heart disease, heart attack or anxiety, depression or even awaken latent disorders, and contribute to psychotic episodes – breakdown.

So, stress and health can create a vicious circle: poor health leads to stress and greater stress leads to poorer health. This is often the case when we are out of work. Lack of work has been shown to be bad for your health. It can be difficult to take control of your life, to continue to make all those job applications and to recognise opportunities when they arise.

And the reverse is true, good health can help reduce stress, through physical fitness and mental resilience.

So, what helped me?

Based on my experience, I'd suggest two paths in parallel: creativity and mindfulness. The first I've experienced as a writer and poet, the second I am still learning.

And to close, there is also in a sense, that universal, underlying stress – the knowledge that we are not here forever. And yet, that is arguably one of the most profound reasons for enjoying life, putting our worries into perspective and living in the moment. We are all unique in our appreciation of life, if only it were possible to more widely celebrate our diversity and eliminate stigma.

12 June 2014

⇨ The above information is reprinted with kind permission from Time to Change. Please visit www.time-to-change.org.uk for further information.

How women experience stress: what the research tells us

Studies show that women are more likely to feel anxious or sad – and that women rely more on their social circles than men.

By Nadja Popvich

Several recent studies have come to the same conclusion: at work, and in general, women are feeling the pressures of stress more than their male peers.

Whether it's anxiety, a feeling of failure, or the need to binge-eat a sleeve of Oreo cookies, the experience of stress varies from person to person, but there are also themes that connect women's experience of stress.

For one, that stomach-churning anxiety is far more common in women than men.

A 2008 study led by Yale's Dr Tara Chaplin, whose research focuses on the role of gender and emotion, found that women are more likely than men to feel sad and anxious because of stress. Women are also more likely to ruminate on those negative feelings.

When we asked our female readers about their experience with stress last week, many of the 80 responders reported such feelings of anxiety or sadness.

The propensity to dwell on negative emotions, internalise stress and blame yourself may constrain many women's ability to work through stressful situations.

"If you think about it, sadness and anxiety are very passive emotions. If you're sitting there feeling sad and anxious, you're not as likely to problem-solve and be assertive. That could be a problem in the workplace," Chaplin told *The Guardian*.

Studies have also found that women rely more on their social circles than men when stressed. An oft-noted 2000 study found that women more often respond to stressful situations through a model dubbed 'tend-and-befriend', while men follow the 'fight-or-flight' model.

Dr Lynn F Buska, assistant executive director of research and policy for the American Psychological Association and a member of the APA's Stress in America survey team, explained: 'Women tend to reach out for social support when stressed; they look to protect those around them. That makes sense, too, if you think about the early roles women held – they were the mothers, the caregivers.'

Indeed, many of our readers expressed dealing with their stress by reaching out to others, be it family, friends, co-workers or a partner.

Women's tendency to report higher levels of distress than men in surveys and studies may also be partly due to the way women and men are socialised to express themselves in the US and much of western Europe.

'Women may be more aware of their stress and able to admit it – and men may feel penalized for reporting stress or acknowledging it,' Dr Bufka said.

Other ways women and men internalise gender roles from a young age may inform their relationship with stress, too.

Often, girls are taught to 'think more about relationships, and subvert their needs toward the group's needs or towards others. Whereas boys are socialized earlier on to be more assertive and expressive about their needs,' Bufka said. These attitudes can transfer to adult experiences, which may help explain why men report being better able to balance personal demands with work.

It is difficult to unpack the influence of such socialisation from biological reasons why women may be more prone to feeling stressed than men. But one thing is true: women are consistently reporting higher levels of stress than their male peers – and as their presence in the workforce and role in society continues to expand, there is a good chance they will continue to feel the pressure.

Dr Chaplin suggested that women – and in fact, just about anyone feeling stressed – use more active methods of coping, rather than succumb to negative emotions.

'Rather than just sit there and feel stressed and sad, try and think 'OK, well what can I change about this situation to make myself less stressed?' Or 'What coping techniques can I use to make myself feel better?' Take an active role and thinking of healthy ways to cope – which could be anything from exercise, meditating, using some new mindfulness techniques, taking breaks for yourself,' she said.

Yet, while it is important for women to learn how to cope with stress at work and at home, Chaplin noted that it is also important not to blame women for feeling stressed.

'I focus my research on how women and men cope with stress, but we also need to have a conversation about what can be done societally to reduce stress on women,' she said. 'Are there programs that can be in place for subsidising daycare so you have good daycare? Could we have longer maternity leave? These sorts of things are really important.'

14 March 2013

⇨ The above information is reprinted with kind permission from *The Guardian*. Please visit www.theguardian.com for further information.

Depressed, anxious, lonely and homesick: study reveals darker side to student life

By Adam Mason

A new study released by the Nightline Association suggests negative feelings and mood states including depression, anxiety, and stress are prevalent in the UK's student population.

A nationally representative sample of 1,000 university students found that 75% of them had personally experienced some kind of emotional distress while at university. Stress topped the list at 65% whilst 43% of students stated that they had experienced anxiety, loneliness and feelings of not being able to cope. Around one third of students had felt depressed or homesick at some time whilst 29% had worried about not fitting in at university.

Of those surveyed, one in 12 stated that they had experienced suicidal thoughts – nearly half of which (45%) were based in the Midlands or Scotland.

The research, conducted by YouthSight, also found that of the students who reported negative feelings, around one third (32%) had experienced them at night – a time when other specialist welfare services are usually closed.

Mags Godderidge, Charity Development Manager states: 'This research gives us an interesting insight into student wellbeing. Only 5% of students surveyed agreed with the statement "No, I don't know anyone who has experienced these feelings whilst at university"'suggesting these negative feelings and mood states are prevalent in the UK student population. That so many students are feeling anxious, depressed, lonely and homesick during the night only further supports the need for services like Nightline'.

Last November, data from the Office for National Statistics published by Mental Wealth UK revealed that student suicides had doubled over a four-year period between the years 2007–2011, whilst last month results from a NUS survey indicated high levels of stress and anxiety in the student population.

Teddy Woodhouse, Head of External Communications, and a former Nightline listening volunteer at St Andrews said: 'All Nightlines are run by students for students. We know that university is a time of many changes and challenges so we can empathise with service users. Our specially trained volunteers listen to whatever it is that is troubling a student caller. Given that Nightline is confidential and anonymous, students accessing the service don't have to give their name.'

Hannah Paterson, NUS Disabled Students Officer, said: 'I think that the Nightline survey confirms much of the findings of the recent NUS mental health research. Three quarters of the Nightline respondents states that they had experienced some kind of emotional distress whilst at university. It was clear from the NUS findings that mental health is something that needs to be addressed on UK campuses, and this survey serves to compound that assertion. NUS is currently meeting with mental health organisations in a bid to bring all stakeholders together to examine the standard of mental health care in UK universities.'

4 June 2013

⇨ The above information is reprinted with kind permission from Nightline and YouthSight. Please visit www.nightline.ac.uk for further information.

Girls under stress age more rapidly, new Stanford study reveals

Girls at high risk for developing depression have greater stress responses and shorter telomeres – a marker for aging – than their low-risk peers.

By Rex Sanders

Stress takes a toll on both mind and body.

Intuitively, that's not a big surprise. Many studies have found links among stress, depression and disease. But scientists didn't really know which came first: stress, depression or changes in the body.

Stanford psychologist Ian Gotlib and colleagues at Stanford, Northwestern University and the University of California, San Francisco found one way to address this question. They studied healthy girls at high risk for developing depression because they have a family history of the disorder. These girls were stressed out, and they responded to stress by releasing much higher levels of the hormone cortisol.

The girls also had telomeres that were shorter by the equivalent of six years in adults. Telomeres are caps on the ends of chromosomes. Every time a cell divides the telomeres get a little shorter. Telomere length is like a biological clock corresponding to age. Telomeres also shorten as a result of exposure to stress. Scientists have uncovered links in adults between shorter telomeres and premature death, more frequent infections and chronic diseases.

Gotlib, the David Starr Jordan Professor and chair of the Department of Psychology, was surprised by the telomere shortening: "I did not think that these girls would have shorter telomeres than their low-risk counterparts – they're too young."

So which came first: stress, depression or premature aging? These otherwise healthy girls showed signs of stress and premature aging before any of them were old enough to develop depression.

Girls under stress

For this study, published recently in *Molecular Psychiatry*, the team recruited ten to 14-year-old healthy girls with a family history of depression and compared them to healthy girls without that background.

The researchers measured the girls' response to stress tests, asking them to count backwards from 100 by sevens, and interviewing them about stressful situations. Before and after the test, the team measured the girls' cortisol levels. They also analysed DNA samples for telomere length.

Before this study, 'No one had examined telomere length in young children who are at risk for developing depression,' Gotlib said.

Healthy but high-risk 12-year-old girls had significantly shorter telomeres, a sign of premature aging.

'It's the equivalent in adults of six years of biological aging,' Gotlib said, but 'it's not at all clear that that makes them 18, because no one has done this measurement in children.'

Preventive actions

What can a concerned parent or guardian do? Gotlib noted that other research shows exercise delays telomere shortening in adults, and he recommended that high-risk girls learn stress reduction techniques.

In other studies, Gotlib and his team are examining the effectiveness of stress reduction techniques for girls. Neurofeedback and attention bias training (redirecting attention toward the positive) seem promising. Other investigators are studying techniques based on mindfulness training.

The researchers are continuing to monitor the girls from the original study. 'It's looking like telomere length is predicting who's going to become depressed and who's not,' Gotlib said.

28 October 2014

⇨ The above information is reprinted with kind permission from Stanford. Please visit news.stanford.edu for further information.

My carefree child developed generalised anxiety disorder

One in ten children in the UK suffer from mental health problems.

This time last year, our happy-go-lucky third child departed for secondary school. Confident, carefree and smiley, she was eager to join her older sister.

Within months, she had developed generalised anxiety disorder (see below) and it's only now, 12 months later, that we are on the road to getting our daughter back.

When you have a baby, you are overwhelmed with an overload of information. Feeding, sleeping, weaning, walking, potty training – the list of things to master is endless. But there's info out there and it's easy to chat, sometimes even to strangers, about what worked for them and what may help you and your baby.

But when your child gets bigger, and you are faced with something around which there is still a huge amount of stigma – it can be a lonely, frightening and altogether scarier affair.

This week Dame Sally Davies, England's Chief Medical Officer, published her annual report. What she had to say rang all too chillingly familiar with me.

Her report highlighted the greater need for earlier treatment for children and young people with mental health problems.

'Half of adult mental illness starts before the age of 15, and 75 per cent by the age of 18. Unless young people get help, they risk a life of problems including unemployment, substance misuse, crime and antisocial behaviour.

'Under-investment in mental health services, particularly for young people, simply does not make sense economically,' she said.

This is so true.

Our daughter – let's call her Hannah – came home on day two of secondary school, and announced with steely determination, 'I don't like that school and I'm not going back'.

No amount of talking, cajoling, comforting or indeed, ignoring, could jog her out of her own feeling of impending doom.

I don't know anyone else who has a child who has suddenly entered the world of mental health issues.

Or at least, I may do, but you can bet I don't know who they are.

Had Hannah broken her leg, developed severe tonsillitis or been diagnosed with a wheat or nut allergy, I'm pretty sure I could have turned to numerous friends and family for advice.

And if it's something that as a family you have never come across, then it's a real case of the blind leading the blind.

Something that really struck me is that I've since found out one in ten children in the UK aged five to 16 suffer from a diagnosable mental health disorder.

That equates to around three children in every average-size class.

And even more worrying – and a statistic that backs up Dame Sally's findings – is that 95 per cent of imprisoned young offenders have a mental health disorder.

Why then was it so difficult to access speedy help which may have prevented us finally having to remove our daughter from school and placing her in a new environment, which could have simply exacerbated the situation, but was, in fact, the only option left to us?

What we did

In our case, the initial approaches to the school were met with robust rebuttals, that Hannah was just having teething problems and that there wasn't a problem.

Deaf to my pleas that she was demonstrating increasingly erratic behaviour at home and also on the journey to and from school as reported to me by my other daughter, I went away to lick my wounds, afraid I would be labelled a helicopter mum.

I even bought a joke book and left it lying around Hannah's bedroom. I thought it might cheer her up.

Now I shudder to recollect this clumsy attempt – one of so many tactics we tried, including sending Hannah to a counsellor.

This particular person seemed more interested in her own problems than helping our daughter articulate hers, but we were desperate to solve an issue, which we were way out of our depth on.

We invited Hannah's friends round but would have to cancel as she refused to let anyone into her room and we tried the 'she'll wear herself out eventually and we'll all be back to normal' tactic.

But when my sister dropped in unexpectedly one evening while Hannah was having a complete tantrum about homework, and was horrified at the scene that beset her, I knew it was time to up the ante.

And this is where we really struggled.

As a journalist I am used to asking questions and not taking no for an answer. I'm equally used to digging deep to find answers and yes, I suppose getting what I want in difficult situations – persuasive but polite conversation is a skill I like to think I've honed.

But this was something else altogether.

Numerous meetings with school (including a mortifying moment for Hannah when she was publicly hooked out of class by the school counsellor) and a number of visits to the GP, sometimes with Hannah and sometimes without, proved fruitless for weeks.

But by Christmas, when our older daughter reported she could no longer be responsible for accompanying her sister to and from school, I went to see the GP again.

At this stage Hannah was still just about holding it together at school, but at home family life was reduced to a hotbed of tears, closed doors (her siblings kept well away) and sobs.

One GP (because of course these days you never see the same one twice) told Hannah she must simply pull herself together and 'stop being silly'.

I will never, ever forget that moment. My husband visibly stiffened as I took a deep intake of breath and declared my intention, quite calmly, not to leave the surgery until she could produce some kind of plan.

She eventually and reluctantly agreed to write us a referral to CAMHS (the NHS child and adolescent mental health services) but since it was Christmas we had to wait until after the holidays for an emergency appointment.

By the time we took a sleep-deprived, withdrawn and apprehensive Hannah to see the specialist, our daughter was finally unable to keep herself composed and it all came tumbling out. But even then we struggled to get the psychologist to grasp the gravity of the situation.

There were a number of other children in the waiting room and I felt this woman just needed to get through her list of patients.

Looking back at this moment, Dame Sally's view that under-investment in mental health services, particularly for young people, simply does not make sense economically is all too shudderingly true.

In economic terms to the NHS alone, time and money spent on our daughter now, would surely be less than if this progressed into adulthood.

At Hannah's second meeting with the CAMHS lady, she was brutally honest with us:

'Your daughter is, for whatever reason, in a toxic situation,' she said. 'My advice, if it's possible, is that you remove her from an environment that is clearly having such a detrimental effect on her mental health, look around for a different school, and consider a course of CBT.'

At the time I thought she was abrupt, rude and lacking in compassion, but by that stage I was pretty run down myself and would have tried anything.

So to cut a still pretty long story short, we embraced the advice and went for it, and finally, after our own long winter of discontent, we turned a very small corner and Lady Luck finally appeared.

We were incredibly lucky to manage to get Hannah into a different school nearer to home, and there staff simply told her she merely had to turn up each day. Nothing more was required of her – no homework, no expectations were made of her at all.

And we, rightly or wrongly, turned down a wait on the NHS and because we could, Hannah went off to see a lady who I now owe not only my daughter's sanity to, but mine as well.

Our daughter has completed a 12-week course of Cognitive Behavioural Therapy (see below) and is working hard on maintaining this new state of mind.

Crucially, Hannah now has a set of strategies for coping with change and stress, which will hopefully serve her for life. And she is learning to live in the present – neither brooding on the past or worrying about the future.

I just wish someone had listened to us sooner.

What is Generalised Anxiety Disorder?

Generalised Anxiety Disorder (GAD) can be defined as a disorder in which the sufferer feels in a constant state of high anxiety and is often known as 'chronic worrying' or a 'free floating' anxiety condition.

People who suffer with GAD often resolve one issue, but no sooner has this been done when another worry pops up. Racing thoughts, loss of concentration, and an inability to focus are also characteristic of this condition.

We all suffer with worry from time to time, but the thing that makes GAD different from 'normal worry' is that the worry is prolonged (it lasts for more than six months), and the level of worry is out of proportion to the risk.

For example, a child with GAD may feel the need to do all their homework to absolute perfection for fear of getting into trouble, and will spend far more time on it than is at all necessary. Or they may think somebody at school hates them, and is telling everyone else to, just because the child accidently bumped into them.

These thoughts can be described as 'catastrophising', or jumping to the worst possible conclusion.

GAD is a particularly difficult condition to live with, as it is constantly on the sufferer's mind – there is no respite as the anxiety is not tied to a specific situation or event. It can cause problems with sleep, ability to maintain a job or do any work, as well as impact on close relationships.

What is Cognitive Behavioural Therapy?

Cognitive Behavioural Therapy (CBT) is a talking therapy that can help you manage your problems by changing the way you think and behave.

It is most commonly used to treat anxiety and depression, but can be useful for other mental and physical health problems.

CBT cannot remove your problems, but it can help you deal with them in a more positive way. It is based on the concept that your thoughts, feelings, physical sensations and actions are interconnected, and that negative thoughts and feelings can trap you in a vicious cycle.

CBT aims to help you crack this cycle by breaking down overwhelming problems into smaller parts and showing you how to change these negative patterns to improve the way you feel.

Unlike some other talking treatments, CBT deals with your current problems, rather than focusing on issues from your past. It looks for practical ways to improve your state of mind on a daily basis.

Top tips for talking to your children about anxiety:

Seize the moment – it doesn't have to be a formal interview. Chat over a meal, in the car, as you do the supermarket shop – keep it light and casual. You don't have to spend hours talking.

Mental health is no less important than our physical health. Encourage your child to talk about her feelings, and if a certain situation has really upset her, explore it with her. What might she do to feel better about it? How might she resolve it? How does she learn to manage to keep it in proportion? How does that worrying thought make her feel, and how does it bear on their actions?

Show him strategies for getting away from it all and chilling. Talking, exercise, me time, time away from social media and homework pressures are all positives which will help them keep a balance.

Keep it casual – avoid jargon and if you have to dumb down, so be it. Let her know nothing can shock you and that you are there for her. Equally, don't let her take up all your time going over the same issue. When she is in a negative circle of worry, agree to discuss it and then move on.

Don't make it too personal. If you suspect your child is worrying about something, but doesn't want to open up, generalise and hypothesise instead. Or talk about a character from a book or a TV programme he likes. 'How would X respond to this?'

Let him know it's OK to find out more together. Look at some websites – there is a lot of information out there and they may be especially comforted to read other young peoples' stories about their own mental health issues.

⇨ The above information is reprinted with kind permission from Parent Dish. Please visit www.parentdish.co.uk for further information.

Young people with anxiety

Anxiety is a condition that can affect anyone – it doesn't distinguish between age, background or social group. Even some of the most confident people you know may have suffered with anxiety. Recent research suggests that as many as one in six young people will experience an anxiety condition at some point in their lives, this means that up to five people in your class may be living with anxiety, whether that be OCD (obsessive compulsive disorder), social anxiety and shyness, exam stress, worry or panic attacks.

Many anxiety disorders begin in childhood and adolescence, and the average time a person waits to seek help for their condition (particularly for OCD and chronic worrying or GAD as it is known) is over ten years! That is a long time to be feeling anxious. You can save yourself a lot of stress by getting help sooner rather than later. At Anxiety UK we have trained volunteers who have lived with anxiety themselves. They are available Monday to Friday 9.30–5.30 and can help you decide what a good next step is for you. You don't have to suffer in silence.

There are also a number of services and resources that are designed for young people which you can access by becoming a member of Anxiety UK. If you do not wish to become a member, you can still access information and support through our email information service and national helpline.

It can often be difficult to discuss how you feel with other people, especially if you think that no one else feels the same, or that they won't understand. You may feel that you don't fully understand what is happening to you, which can make it very hard to explain to others exactly what you are going through. Often, experiencing anxiety can leave you feeling tired, upset and frustrated. This can make you feel that you are unable to cope or that there is nothing that you can do to improve the situation.

Anxiety can affect us all in very different ways. Experiences of anxiety can vary greatly from person to person and no two people are the same. If you feel that any of the experiences or symptoms described on these pages apply to you, then we may be able to help.

First of all, anxiety is completely normal! It is something that we all experience to some level. Anxiety is useful to us as it tells us that something is dangerous and that we need to be careful. However, if anxiety gets out of control or stops you from doing everyday things, then this can lead to us feeling unhappy, upset and frustrated.

Here are some examples of how you might feel if you are anxious:

⇨ Worried

⇨ Upset

⇨ Feeling sick

⇨ Feeling shaky/dizzy

⇨ Feeling like you might faint/pass out

⇨ Thinking unpleasant thoughts

⇨ Thinking that you might 'go crazy'

When anxiety gets really strong, you might experience what we call a 'panic attack'. This is when your body is getting ready to fight, freeze or to run away from the situation that we are viewing as dangerous. This is known as the fight, flight or freeze response. Again, it can be quite scary to experience, although we know that it will not hurt you.

One of the ways to reduce the anxiety that you are feeling is to understand it better. By understanding how anxiety works, you can then understand why you feel that way and it will help you to break the vicious circle of anxiety that just makes things worse.

The 'fear of the fear' often makes us feel worse as we are literally on edge waiting for bad feelings to happen; we stop doing things that we link with the negative (bad) feelings or thoughts. This is called avoidance. The more that we avoid the thing that we link with feeling bad, the more we think of it as being dangerous.

This means that the next time we have to face the situation or event, our body tells us that it is dangerous and the fight, flight or freeze response kicks in. We feel that we either need to run away from the 'dangerous' thing, fight it or we feel that our body is frozen to the spot.

Either way, our body is not happy when we feel all of these horrible feelings and think horrible things. By understanding why we feel this way, we can then take away the 'scared' feeling because we know that it is just our body reacting to something that it thinks is scary, even though it is actually harmless. No-one ever died from having anxiety!

Getting help

The good news is that anxiety is treatable! This means that there are things that can be done to reduce feelings of anxiety. The first step is to speak to someone that you trust about how you are feeling. This could be a teacher, a parent, a relative or another adult that you trust. Talking to someone will reduce the pressure of anxiety and stress, it may also help you to realise that you are not alone in how you are feeling.

Talking to others

Often, because the anxious feelings and thoughts are so bad, we don't want to tell anyone how we feel as we believe that they might not understand or they might laugh at us. However, this is the best way to get help to change how you feel. By looking at this article, you are already aware that you are not happy with how things are. Talking to someone about how you feel can help.

⇨ Choose someone that you trust; for example, a parent/ family member/teacher, etc.

⇨ Tell them how you have been feeling and try to give them an example so that they understand clearly.

⇨ If you are finding it hard to talk about this, try writing them a letter or showing them this article.

⇨ Remember: It is OK to be upset and it is OK to ask for help

Once you have spoken to someone, they will be able to get help for you.

You can also call Anxiety UK Helpline number: 08444 775 774 to talk to someone in complete confidence between 9.30 and 5.30, Monday to Friday.

⇨ The above information is reprinted with kind permission from AnxietyUK. Please visit www.anxietyuk.org.uk for further information.

Only one in 20 people never feel anxious.

Almost one in five people feel anxious all of the time or a lot of the time.

Comfort eating is used by a quarter of people to cope with feelings of anxiety.

The most commonly used coping strategies are talking to a friend, going for a walk and physical exercise.

Younger people are much more likely to feel anxious about personal relationships.

Four in every ten employed people experience anxiety about their work.

Source: YouGov survey of 2,300 adults in Britain, mental health week 2014

What are anxiety disorders?

There are various conditions (disorders) where anxiety is a main symptom. You may have an anxiety disorder if anxiety symptoms interfere with your normal day-to-day activities, or if worry about developing anxiety symptoms affects your life. About one in 20 people have an anxiety disorder at any one time. The following is a brief overview of the main anxiety disorders. Some people have features of more than one type of disorder.

Reactions to stress

Anxiety can be one of a number of symptoms as a reaction to stressful situations. There are three common types of reaction disorders:

Acute reaction to stress (sometimes called acute stress reaction)

Acute means the symptoms develop quickly, over minutes or hours, reacting to the stressful event. Acute reactions to stress typically occur after an unexpected life crisis such as an accident, bereavement, family problem, bad news, etc.

Sometimes symptoms occur before a known situation which is difficult. This is called situational anxiety. This may occur, for example, before an examination, an important race, a concert performance, etc.

Symptoms usually settle fairly quickly, but can sometimes last for several days or weeks. Apart from anxiety, other symptoms include low mood, irritability, emotional ups and downs, poor sleep, poor concentration, wanting to be alone.

Adjustment reaction

This is similar to the above, but symptoms develop days or weeks after a stressful situation, as a reaction or adjustment to the problem. For example, as a reaction to a divorce or house move. Symptoms are similar to acute reaction to stress but may include depression. The symptoms tend to improve over a few weeks or so.

Post-traumatic stress disorder

Post-traumatic stress disorder (PTSD) may follow a severe trauma such as a serious assault or life-threatening accident. Symptoms last at least one month, often much

longer. Anxiety is only one symptom which may come and go. The main symptoms of PTSD are:

⇨ Recurring thoughts, memories, images, dreams, or flashbacks of the trauma, which are distressing.

⇨ You try to avoid thoughts, feelings, conversations, places, people, activities or anything else which may trigger memories or thoughts of the trauma.

⇨ Feeling emotionally numb and detached from others. You may find it difficult to have loving feelings.

⇨ Your outlook for the future is often pessimistic. You may lose interest in activities which you used to enjoy.

⇨ Increased arousal which you did not have before the trauma. This may include difficulty sleeping, being irritable, difficulty concentrating, and increased vigilance.

Phobic anxiety disorders

A phobia is strong fear or dread of a thing or event. The fear is out of proportion to the reality of the situation. Coming near or into contact with the feared situation causes anxiety. Sometimes even thinking of the feared situation causes anxiety. Therefore, you end up avoiding the feared situation, which can restrict your life and may cause suffering.

Social anxiety disorder

Social anxiety disorder (also known as social phobia) is possibly the most common phobia. With social anxiety disorder you become very anxious about what other people may think of you, or how they may judge you. Therefore, you fear meeting people, or 'performing' in front of other people, especially strangers. You fear that you will act in an embarrassing way, and that

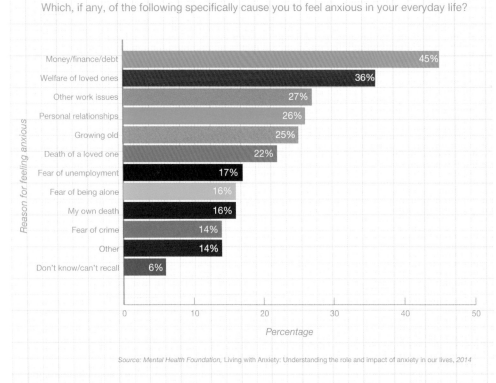

Which, if any, of the following specifically cause you to feel anxious in your everyday life?

Reason for feeling anxious	Percentage
Money/finance/debt	45%
Welfare of loved ones	36%
Other work issues	27%
Personal relationships	26%
Growing old	25%
Death of a loved one	22%
Fear of unemployment	17%
Fear of being alone	16%
My own death	16%
Fear of crime	14%
Other	14%
Don't know/can't recall	6%

Source: Mental Health Foundation, Living with Anxiety: Understanding the role and impact of anxiety in our lives, 2014

other people will think that you are stupid, inadequate, weak, foolish, crazy, etc. You avoid such situations as much as possible. If you go to the feared situation you become very anxious and distressed.

Agoraphobia

This too is common. Many people think that agoraphobia means a fear of public places and open spaces. But this is just part of it. If you have agoraphobia you tend to have a number of fears of various places and situations. So, for example, you may have a fear of:

⇨ Entering shops, crowds and public places.

⇨ Travelling in trains, buses or planes.

⇨ Being on a bridge or in a lift.

⇨ Being in a cinema, restaurant, etc, where there is no easy exit.

But they all stem from one underlying fear. That is, a fear of being in a place where help will not be available, or where you feel it may be difficult to escape to a safe place (usually to your home). When you are in a feared place you become very anxious and distressed, and have an intense desire to get out. To avoid this anxiety many people with agoraphobia stay inside their home for most or all of the time.

Other specific phobias

There are many other phobias of a specific thing or situation. For example:

⇨ Fear of confined spaces or of being trapped (claustrophobia).

⇨ Fear of certain animals.

⇨ Fear of injections.

⇨ Fear of vomiting.

⇨ Fear of being alone.

⇨ Fear of choking.

But there are many more.

Other anxiety disorders

Panic disorder

Panic disorder means that you get recurring panic attacks. A panic attack is a severe attack of anxiety

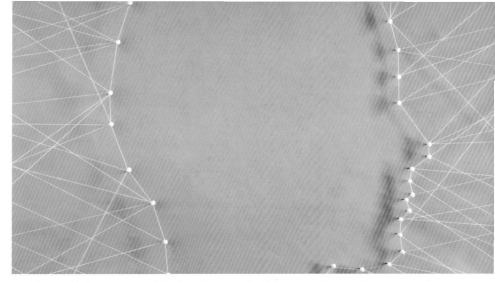

and fear which occurs suddenly, often without warning, and for no apparent reason. The physical symptoms of anxiety during a panic attack can be severe and include a thumping heart (palpitations), trembling, feeling short of breath, chest pains, feeling faint, numbness, or pins and needles. Each panic attack usually lasts 5-10 minutes, but sometimes they come in waves for up to two hours.

Generalised anxiety disorder

If you have generalised anxiety disorder (GAD) you have a lot of anxiety (feeling fearful, worried and tense) on most days. The condition persists long-term. Some of the physical symptoms of anxiety (detailed above) may come and go. Your anxiety tends to be about various stresses at home or work, often about quite minor things. Sometimes you do not know why you are anxious. In addition, you will usually have three or more of the following symptoms:

⇨ Feeling restless, on edge, or 'keyed up' a lot of the time.

⇨ Tiring easily.

⇨ Difficulty concentrating and your mind going blank quite often.

⇨ Being irritable a lot of the time.

⇨ Muscle tension.

⇨ Poor sleep (insomnia). Usually it is difficulty in getting off to sleep, or difficulty in staying asleep.

Mixed anxiety and depressive disorder

In some people, anxiety can be a symptom when you have depression. Other symptoms of depression include low mood,

feelings of sadness, sleep problems, poor appetite, irritability, poor concentration, decreased sex drive, loss of energy, guilt feelings, headaches, aches, pains and palpitations. Treatment tends to be aimed mainly at easing depression, and the anxiety symptoms often then ease too.

Obsessive-compulsive disorder

Obsessive-compulsive disorder (OCD) consists of recurring obsessions, compulsions, or both.

⇨ Obsessions are recurring thoughts, images or urges that cause you anxiety or disgust. Common obsessions are fears about dirt, contamination, germs, disasters, violence, etc.

⇨ Compulsions are thoughts or actions that you feel you must do or repeat. Usually a compulsion is a response to ease the anxiety caused by an obsession. A common example is repeated hand washing in response to the obsessional fear about dirt or germs. Other examples of compulsions include repeated cleaning, checking, counting, touching and hoarding of objects.

⇨ Used with permission from Patient.co.uk. Available at http://www.patient.co.uk/health/anxiety

Charity claims 20% of people regularly feel anxious

The Mental Health Foundation has published a report showing that almost one in five people feel anxious either a lot or all of the time.

Mike Brent, a Care UK recovery specialist, explains what can trigger feelings of anxiety and offers advice on how to deal with the condition, which is one of the most prevalent mental health problems in the UK.

Published last month, *Living with Anxiety – understanding the role and impact of anxiety in our lives* explores what can trigger feelings of anxiety, how it can be exacerbated by modern life, and the impact it can have on people's lives. A survey conducted as part of the report also revealed that of the people affected by anxiety, two thirds of them experience the emotion on a daily basis.

To help increase people's understanding of anxiety, this year's Mental Health Awareness Week (12–18 May) focused on the condition and its effect on the mental health and wellbeing of people throughout the country.

Care UK runs a range of services for people living with long-term mental health conditions. It offers expert support that is delivered using a person-centred approach designed to involve people in the planning and provision of their treatment. Mike Brent, clinical quality and audit manager at the independent health and social care provider, offers the following advice for people experiencing feelings of anxiety.

What is anxiety?

Anxiety is completely normal and everyone will experience it at some point in their lives, whether it is before attending a job interview or riding a rollercoaster.

The purpose of anxiety is to prepare for danger by getting the body ready to defend itself or, in a modern day perspective, it helps you perform at your best. It's fair to say that without anxiety, the human race wouldn't survive.

However, anxiety can become a problem when the body reacts to no real danger. This can start to affect people on a day-to-day basis, which in turn affects how people cope with life's daily challenges.

When anxiety or worry feels extreme, it may be a sign of an anxiety disorder. For someone who has an anxiety disorder, getting proper care from a health professional is important. The following tips can help but if you feel things are getting out of control and you have difficulty functioning in daily life as you normally would, professional help is the best course of action.

Sometimes anxiety can cause a panic attack. If your heart rate rises or palms start to sweat the best thing is not to fight it. Stay where you are and simply feel the panic without trying to distract yourself. Placing the palm of your hand on your stomach and breathing slowly and deeply (no more than 12 breaths a minute) helps soothe the body. It may take up to an hour, but eventually the panic will go away on its own. The goal is to help the mind get used to coping with panic, which takes the worry of fear away.

Tips for coping with anxiety

Become a relaxation expert

With our 24/7 society moving at ever increasing speed and with the advent of the Internet, smartphones and being constantly contactable via social media, people have forgotten the art of relaxation. Watching television or accessing the Internet is not true relaxation and depending on what you're watching, could make you more tense or anxious. The body needs true relaxation like deep breathing, tai chi or yoga that has a physical effect on the mind. A moment to close your eyes and imagine a place of safety and calm can enhance positive feelings and help you relax.

Back to basics

Get the right amount of sleep for your needs, not too much or too little. Eat a balanced diet and try to consume foods for long-term energy and not the short bursts that come from sugar or caffeine. Exercise sends oxygen to every cell in the body and will invigorate your body and mind. A good sleep and a balanced meal are often the best cures for anxiety.

Connect with others and talk about it

Spend time with friends and family. Doing things with people we like strengthens bonds and makes us feel supported and secure. Having fun makes us feel happy and less upset about things. Talking about problems helps us to feel understood and cared for and enhances the ability to cope. Likewise, sharing feelings of anxiety can take away their impact. If you can't talk to a friend, family member or partner there are many helplines that can assist

Get outside

Getting away from the hustle and bustle of everyday life can help you feel more peaceful and grounded. Go somewhere you feel safe and can relax and enjoy your surroundings. The great outdoors can help to put things into perspective.

Think positive

Focus on thoughts and feelings that are good and positive. Allow yourself to day dream, wish and imagine the best that could happen.

Take time out

It's impossible to think clearly when you are anxious, with symptoms such as a racing heart, sweating palms, butterflies in your stomach and feeling nervous all being the result of adrenalin. You need to take time out to calm down physically. Walking, having a bath or having a cup of tea can help you physically calm down.

What's the worst that could happen?

Whatever is worrying you, it can help to think about the worst case scenario and plan for it, then, if the worst does happen, you can be ready. Fears tend to be much worse than the reality. For example, people sometimes feel very self- conscious when they blush in social situations and this makes you more anxious. This is a completely normal response and telling yourself this can help in banishing the anxiety.

Don't expect perfection

Unrealistic thoughts and goals can only set us up for anxiety. Life is full of stresses and strains and many people feel that life must be perfect. Bad days and setbacks will always happen and it is essential to remember that life can be messy and disorganised sometimes.

Reward yourself

Give yourself a treat when you have conquered your anxiety, reinforce your success with whatever makes you happy.

10 June 2014

⇨ The above information is reprinted with kind permission from Care UK. Please visit www.careuk.com for further information.

Anxiety: hospital admissions highest in women in their late 60s

Hospital admissions for anxiety increased with age and were highest among older women, new figures from the Health & Social Care Information Centre (HSCIC) show.

Hospital admissions for anxiety increased with age and were highest among older women, new figures from the Health and Social Care Information Centre (HSCIC) show.

In the 12 months to November 2013 almost three out of ten anxiety admissions were women aged 60 and over (2,440 out of 8,720, or 28 per cent), with 65 to 69 the most common age group of female patient admissions (437, or eight per cent of all female admissions). The most common age group for male patient admissions was 45 to 49 (279, or 8.5 per cent of all male admissions).

Today's report also looks at hospital admissions for stress which were highest in girls aged 15 to 19 years (295) and men aged 40 to 44 years (343) and three quarters of patients were under 50 years old (74 per cent or 3,580 out of 4,840).

The pattern of admissions for anxiety or stress by age and gender was similar to the previous 12 months; however, total admissions fell by over two per cent for anxiety (from 8,930 to 8,720) and almost 14 per cent for stress (from 5,610 to 4,840).

The overall trend in admissions by age showed that anxiety admissions increased with age and stress admissions amongst adults aged 45 years and above decreased with age.

The report published today focuses on a special topic which is part of a wider monthly publication of all NHS-commissioned provisional inpatient, outpatient and A&E activity in England. For all hospital admissions for anxiety or stress between December 2012 and November 2013:

⇨ Women accounted for three in five anxiety admissions (62 per cent or 5,440) whereas more than half of stress admissions were men (55 per cent or 2,660) and this was similar to the previous 12 months (63 per cent and 55 per cent, respectively).

⇨ Almost nine out of ten anxiety cases (89 per cent or 7,750) and eight out of ten stress cases (78 per cent or 3,760) were emergency admissions.

⇨ One in five anxiety cases were diagnosed with high blood pressure (19 per cent or 1,660) and one in four stress admissions had a personal history of self-harm (25 per cent or 1,230).

⇨ Merseyside Area Team had the highest rate of admissions for anxiety and stress (29.7 and 18.4 per 100,000 of the population) and Thames Valley Area Team had the lowest rate of admissions for both conditions (7.2 and 2.0 per 100,000, respectively).

Alan Perkins, CEO of the HSCIC, said: 'Today's report shows striking age patterns in admissions for anxiety, and some interesting age and gender patterns for stress cases.

'Hospitals have dealt with fewer admissions for anxiety and stress compared to last year but the higher rates of anxiety in the older generation could be an area for concern.'

19 February 2014

⇨ © 2013, the above information is reused with the permission of the Health & Social Care Information Centre. All rights reserved. Please visit www. hscic.gov.uk for further information.

Living with anxiety

Understanding the role and impact of anxiety in our lives.

An extract from the report by the Mental Health Foundation

Executive summary

Anxiety is a familiar emotion because it is part of everyone's experience. Its natural function is to alert us to potential threats, allowing us to evaluate and respond to them in appropriate ways. This heightened state of readiness can also help people perform better and stimulate creative impulses. Anxiety is often regarded as an artefact of modern societies, one that is increasingly represented in visual arts, music, literature and social media.

For some people anxiety triggers inappropriate or disproportionate responses to perceived threats, leading to persistent and intrusive symptoms associated with anxiety disorders, such as panic, phobias and obsessive behaviours, which often have a debilitating effect on their lives. Anxiety is one of the most prevalent mental health problems in the UK and elsewhere, yet it is still under-reported, under-diagnosed and under-treated. This report explores the intersection between popular perceptions of anxiety, the experience of anxiety in people's everyday lives and the impact of anxiety disorders.

The experience of anxiety often involves interconnected symptoms and disorders. It is estimated that one in four people in the UK will experience a mental health problem each year, while one in six experience a neurotic disorder such as anxiety or depression. Anxiety disorders are also estimated to affect 3.3% of children and young adults in the UK. The prevalence of the most common forms of anxiety are given below.

⇨ While 2.6% of the population experience depression and 4.7% have anxiety problems, as many as 9.7% suffer mixed depression and anxiety, making it the most prevalent mental health problem in the population as a whole.

⇨ About 1.2% of the UK population experience panic disorders, rising to 1.7% for those experiencing it with or without agoraphobia.

⇨ Around 1.9% of British adults experience a phobia of some description, and women are twice as likely to be affected by this problem as men.

⇨ Agoraphobia affects between 1.5% and 3.5% of the general population in its fully developed form; in a less severe form, up to one in eight people experience this.

⇨ Post-Traumatic Stress Disorder (PTSD) affects 2.6% of men and 3.3% of women.

⇨ Obsessive Compulsive Disorders (OCD) affect around 2–3% of the population.

⇨ Generalised Anxiety Disorder affects between 2–5% of the population, yet accounts for as much as 30% of the mental health problems seen by GPs.

Previous survey evidence suggests that:

⇨ Although, on average, women rate their life satisfaction higher than men, their anxiety levels are significantly higher than men.

⇨ People in their middle years (35 to 59) report the highest levels of anxiety compared to other age groups.

⇨ People in the older age groups tend to be happier and less anxious.

⇨ People with a disability are, on average, more anxious than people without a disability.

⇨ Unemployed people report significantly higher anxiety levels than those in employment.

⇨ People in the lowest income groups report significantly higher anxiety levels than those in the higher income groups.

⇨ On average, all ethnic groups report higher levels of anxiety than people who describe themselves as White British.

⇨ Young people aged 16–24 are more likely to report lower levels of anxiety compared with adults generally.

⇨ Women and young adults aged 20–29 are the most likely to seek help for anxiety from their GP.

Our specially commissioned survey of over 2,000 members of the public found that:

⇨ Almost one in five people feel anxious all of the time or a lot of the time.

⇨ Only one in twenty people never feel anxious.

⇨ Women are more likely to feel anxious than men.

⇨ The likelihood of feeling anxious reduces with age.

⇨ Students and people not in employment are more likely to feel anxious all of the time or a lot of the time.

⇨ Financial issues are a cause of anxiety for half of people, but this is less likely to be so for older people.

⇨ Women and older people are more likely to feel anxious about the welfare of loved ones.

⇨ Four in every ten employed people experience anxiety about their work.

⇨ Around a fifth of people who are anxious have a fear of unemployment.

⇨ Younger people are much more likely to feel anxious about personal relationships.

⇨ Older people are more likely to be anxious about growing old, the death of a loved one and their own death.

⇨ The youngest people surveyed (aged 18–24) were twice as likely to be anxious about being alone than the oldest people (aged over 55 years).

One-fifth of people who have experienced anxiety do nothing to cope with it.

⇨ The most commonly used coping strategies are talking to a friend, going for a walk and physical exercise.

⇨ Comfort eating is used by a quarter of people to cope with feelings of anxiety, and women and young people are more likely to use this as a way of coping.

⇨ A third of the students in the survey said they cope by 'hiding themselves away from the world'.

⇨ People who are unemployed are more likely to use coping strategies that are potentially harmful, such as alcohol and cigarettes.

⇨ Fewer than one in ten people have sought help from their GP to deal with anxiety, although those who feel anxious more frequently are much more likely to do this.

⇨ People are believed to be more anxious now than they were five years ago.

⇨ There is a tendency to reject the notion that having anxious feelings is stigmatising.

⇨ People who experience anxiety most frequently tend to agree that it is stigmatising.

⇨ Just under half of people get more anxious these days than they used to and believe that anxiety has stopped them from doing things in their life.

⇨ Most people want to be less anxious in their day-to-day lives.

⇨ Women and younger people are more likely to say that anxiety has impacted on their lives.

Surveys suggest we live in an 'age of anxiety' which reflects a shared mood about the defining aspects of modern life: our work, the way we raise children, our attitudes to people who are disadvantaged, the future of public services, the threat of terrorism, and so on. At another level, there is evidence of the hidden impact of more severe forms of anxiety upon the lives of a significant number of people. Our understanding of anxiety disorders has improved in recent years due to research, the development of more sophisticated diagnostics, effective treatments, and the emergence of a genuine voice for people living with anxiety. While these developments are encouraging, our own work suggests that there are still gaps that need to be addressed in the provision of support for people who experience anxiety. We recommend a stepped care approach be adopted to ensure that support for living with anxiety is provided in the least stigmatising and most inclusive way possible, including:

⇨ Universal approaches to learning to live well with anxiety should be built into school curriculums from primary one onwards, including an understanding of the role of anxiety in our lives, and techniques for managing stresses associated with school (such as peer relationships, exams and transitions).

⇨ Peer-led approaches should be promoted within universal settings such as employment, schools and universities, in recognition of the importance that young people place on support from peers and the unique level of empathetic understanding that can be provided by those with a common experience.

⇨ Access to good quality self-help approaches should be made available across the UK through quality-assured and co-designed digital platforms to ensure they are fit for purpose for those who choose not to use face-to-face services (young people, people in full-time employment).

⇨ GP training and anxiety-related guidance should be assessed for equalities impact and adapted alongside groups of people who are at highest risk of developing problematic anxiety and least likely to have their needs met by current service provision.

⇨ A sample of psychological services should be audited to establish how well current referral processes are working, who is accessing these, and who is falling through the gaps. This audit should include IAPT (Improving Access to Psychological Therapies) in England and Wales and initiatives to improve access in Scotland.

⇨ Agencies offering support to people with anxiety should make greater use of peer mentors and advice and information that is explicitly based on the life experiences of people who live with anxiety.

We also recommend that research be commissioned to better understand:

⇨ The nature and understanding of anxiety for different groups in society (women, people with long-term conditions, older people, people from black and minority ethnic communities), and whether current approaches and interventions can be found to address specific needs.

⇨ The relationship between unemployment, financial distress and anxiety. The Department of Work and Pensions should develop strategies to prevent people who are not working from becoming marginalised from the workforce. Processes for accessing social welfare for those unable to work due to disability should be assessed for their impact on anxiety levels.

⇨ The impact of technological advancements in self-management for anxiety.

2014

⇨ The above information is reprinted with kind permission from the Mental Health Foundation. Please visit www.mentalhealth.org.uk for further information.

'I burned out from work stress'

Today, Liz Tucker is a health and wellbeing counsellor specialising in stress management. Fourteen years ago, at the age of 30, she burned out from work-related stress.

I had a building company at the time and was working incredibly hard. It wasn't unusual for me to drive from Taunton, up to York and down to Norfolk in the space of 24 hours. I'd start work at 7am and often wouldn't finish until 8pm the following day, 36 hours later. The year I burned out, I drove over 100,000 miles.

'I loved the buzz of it. There was a lot of stress involved, but I really enjoyed the adrenaline kick of having something turn out right in the end. It was very satisfying.

'When the doctor told me I'd burned myself out from too much stress, I found it difficult to believe. To me, stress meant being unhappy, whereas I was really enjoying my life'

'At first the work was manageable. Then, during the year before I became ill, I started working at weekends. I had no social life at all, which didn't bother me at the time.

'Then I met my partner and, because of the pressures of trying to see him and keep on top of the work, it all began to fall apart. I started feeling really tired and very lethargic. One Sunday night I went to bed early because I felt like I was getting a bit of a cold.

'When I woke on Monday, I simply couldn't get out of bed. I could move my fingers, head and feet, but I had no energy in my arms and legs.

'When the doctor told me I'd burned myself out from too much stress, I found it difficult to believe. To me, stress meant being unhappy, whereas I was really enjoying my life. But it was true: there was no work-life balance and I was living a high-stress life.

'In addition, my diet was appalling. I lived on food that I bought in petrol stations, and I hadn't been getting nearly enough sleep. My body had shut itself down in protest.

'For the next three months, I couldn't get out of bed. All I did was sleep. Very slowly, I began to improve but then, after a few months, the doctor diagnosed ME. I was housebound.

'The physical symptoms were bad but the mental 'fog' was awful. It was like someone had drilled a hole in my head and filled it with concrete.

'I was like this for four years, and I was declining. My partner was beginning to wonder whether I was going to die, and when he asked the doctor, the answer was, 'I simply don't know. She has the body of an 80-year-old'. It was very shocking to hear.

'I think, up until that point, I'd believed the doctors knew what was right for me. So hearing that they didn't know what to do made me start thinking about my own future. With my partner, I began thinking about what was right for me to do.

'I decided I needed some pleasure in life. I had been so worried for so long. I began having a weekly massage and hypnotherapy to help me relax. I also decided not to watch anything on TV that was violent or miserable.

'The biggest turning point was when I began to pace myself. Up until then, I'd compare myself to how I was before. If I was feeling a bit better, I would try to do lots of things and then feel ill with

exhaustion again. I began to realise I was setting myself unrealistic goals so I decided to take things gradually.

'Are you stressed by your job? There's a difference between stress and pressure. We all experience pressure daily and need it to motivate us. But too much can lead to damaging stress'

'After I'd started this regime of proper relaxing, it was remarkable how quickly I began to feel better. I was eating a healthy diet with lots of fruit and vegetables and I'd stopped having caffeine and alcohol. I began to notice the changes within a few weeks.

'After three months, I was feeling so much better, but because I'd spent so much time in bed, I was very weak physically.

'After six months, I was back to normal. I had lots of energy, my skin was better and I didn't have to stay in bed the whole time. It was amazing.

'I've now been working as a health and wellbeing counsellor for 10 years. I went back to university and studied human health and biology, really just to find out what had happened to me. I found it so interesting it has turned into my career.

'I'm working really hard again and get a lot of satisfaction out of it, but the difference is that now I have a work-life balance and know what to do when things get too stressful.'

11 April 2013

⇨ The above information is reprinted with kind permission from NHS Choices. Please visit www.nhs.uk for further information.

20% take time off work due to stress

One in five (20%) respondents have taken time off work due to a stress-related illness in the past 12 months, according to research by MetLife Employee Benefits.

Its research, which surveyed 2,134 respondents aged 18 and above, found that one in ten respondents have taken more than six days off work due to stress.

The research found stress was a bigger cause of absence in the past year than sports-related injuries (10%) and hangovers or other alcohol-related issues (8%).

The research also found that nearly two-thirds (63%) of respondents would welcome help and advice from their employer on how to improve their health and well-being.

Currently, 61% of respondents receive some form of health and wellness support at work, with health advice being the most common provision, offered to 37%.

Only 13% are provided with group income protection policies.

Tom Gaynor, employee benefits director at MetLife, said: "Stress is a major issue with one in five employees having to take time off work in the past year.

'It is clear that staff would welcome more support and help from employers on health and wellness in the workplace, and it is also clear that employers have recognised the need to provide support.

'There is a genuine benefit for both employers and employees in promoting good health at work.

'Helping staff to be healthier cuts the cost of absence for employers and enables employees to avoid illness where possible and to recover faster.'

11 April 2014

⇨ The above information is reprinted with kind permission from Employee Benefits. Please visit www.employeebenefits. co.uk for further information.

"..SO, YOU WON'T BE IN TODAY..?"

Mental health costs 'astounding' – and on rise

Around 70 million working days were lost last year because of mental health and England's Chief Medical Officer says the NHS and employers need to do more to help support sufferers at work.

Stress and depression should be treated in the same way as physical health, said Professor Dame Sally Davies, who is calling for a radical rethink in the way it is treated. She has called for funding for these services to be protected, amid warnings that they are being cut, and suggested implementing waiting time targets for treatment.

Dame Sally said the number of working days lost due to stress, depression and anxiety has increased by 24 per cent since 2009, costing an estimated £100 billion and that the number lost due to serious mental illness has doubled.

> **'It is crucial that we take action to help those people stay in employment to benefit their own health as well as the economy'**
>
> *Dame Sally Davies*

Providing a supportive working environment for people with mental health illnesses – for example, allowing more flexible working hours, or part-time working post-illness – could be a key way to prevent sufferers from having to take time off work, she added. An estimated 60 to 70 per cent of people with common mental health disorders were in full-time work.

In her annual report on the mental health of people in England, Dame Sally also said it was striking that three quarters of people with diagnosable mental illness have no treatment at all.

'Treatment gap'

'The costs of mental illness to the economy are astounding,' she said. 'Through this report, I urge commissioners and decision-makers to treat mental health more like physical health.

'The World Health Organization model of mental health promotion, mental illness prevention and treatment and rehabilitation should be adopted in public mental health in England.

'Anyone with mental illness deserves good quality support at the right time.

One of the stark issues highlighted in this report is that 60 to 70 per cent of people with common mental disorders such as depression and anxiety are in work, so it is crucial that we take action to help those people stay in employment to benefit their own health as well as the economy.'

Dr Peter Carter, chief executive and general secretary of the Royal College of Nursing, said: 'The treatment gap for people with mental health problems can no longer be ignored. Not only are people with mental health problems in need of better support for their mental health conditions, but there is an unacceptable and preventable level of correlation with physical ill health.'

9 September 2014

⇨ The above information is reprinted with kind permission from Channel 4 News. Please visit www.channel4.com for further information.

© Channel 4 2015

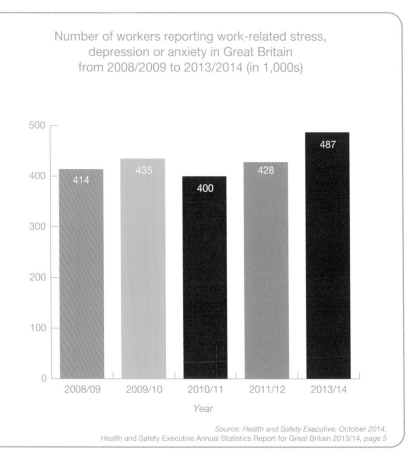

Number of workers reporting work-related stress, depression or anxiety in Great Britain from 2008/2009 to 2013/2014 (in 1,000s)

Source: Health and Safety Executive, October 2014, Health and Safety Executive Annual Statistics Report for Great Britain 2013/14, page 5

Work stress may be causing Brits to drink, smoke and do less exercise, study finds

Stress caused by work may be having a serious negative impact on the nation's health.

That's according to a new study that revealed many people feel work pressures make them drink and smoke more, put on weight and do less exercise.

A survey of almost 1,400 workers revealed that almost a third believed work-related stress could lead to high blood pressure, while one in five feared it could cause a heart attack.

The British Heart Foundation urged employers to encourage workers to spend at least ten minutes a day improving their lifestyle.

Lisa Young, Project Manager for the BHF's Health at Work programme, said: 'This survey is a stark reminder of just what happens when we don't take our health at work seriously enough.

'Millions of people say they are smoking more, exercising less and putting on weight because they're not considering the impact their job is having on their health and wellbeing.

'Behaviours like these can be extremely damaging, not just to your heart health but also to businesses. From working with over 9,500 organisations we know that the pay-offs of making health at work a top businesses priority are too great to ignore.'

A third of those polled said they had put on weight because of work, half ate more unhealthily, a quarter drink more and 43% believe work has caused them to exercise less.

TUC general secretary Frances O'Grady said: 'The BHF report is a shocking indictment of the modern world of work.

'Long hours, the insecurity of jobs on zero-hours contracts and the stress associated with them are all taking a toll on people's health.

'The report's findings show just how bad some workplaces have become. However, the answer is not just for employers to encourage their staff to change their lifestyle - it is for employers to improve working conditions, provide secure jobs and treat their workers like human beings rather than machines.'

12 February 2015

⇨ The above information is reprinted with kind permission from the Press Association. Please visit www.pressassociation.com for further information.

Women 'suffer greater stress and inequality than men at work', global study finds

Women are suffering greater inequality and disadvantages in nearly all aspects of working life, international research has shown.

Researchers said that the results disprove the theory that women have voluntarily traded less high-powered jobs in order to have more flexibility for their responsibilities at home.

In a paper in the journal entitled *Work, Employment and Society*, professor Haya Stier of Tel Aviv University and Professor Meir Yaish from the University of Haifa analysed survey data on the working lives of 8,500 men and 9,000 women across 27 industrialised countries, including the UK. They examined how respondents answered questions about their jobs and found that the answers given disproved commonly held beliefs about women in the workplace.

Women lag behind men on most employment dimensions: their jobs offer lower salaries and fewer opportunities for advancement, but also lower job security, worse job content, less time autonomy and worse emotional conditions, the research found.

As Stier and Yaish expected, men gave answers on questions about income and opportunities for promotion that were on average 8% higher than women's. They also gave answers that were 2% higher than women's when asked about how independently they could work, how interesting they found their work, and how much scope for developing skills they had.

However, the researchers also found that the results 'disproved the theory that women's occupations compensate for their low wages and limited opportunities for promotion by providing better employment conditions'.

When asked about how stressful and exhausting their work was, men gave answers that were 5% lower than women's. On the subject of time autonomy, including having control over when one starts and ends work, men's answers were 15% higher than women's.

Tony Trueman from the British Sociological Association told the Huffington Post UK: 'It's been commonly thought that women take jobs with lower pay and fewer prospects in order to benefit from having more flexibility, so that they have more time to spend at home with their children. This research has proven that women also have less flexibility in the workplace in comparison to men.'

Frances O'Grady, General Secretary of the Trades Union Congress, was 'not surprised' with the finding. She told HuffPostUK: 'These findings will come as no surprise to the millions of working women in the UK involved in the daily juggle between the competing demands of work and caring.

'There are still very few men who give up work or reduce their hours to look after their families,' she added.

4 March 2014

⇨ The above information is reprinted with kind permission from The Huffington Post UK. Please visit www.huffingtonpost.co.uk for further information.

Stress... depress... decompress

Jessica blogs about her experience of stress and how she has found ways of coping.

I'm writing a blog about stress for Stress Awareness Day and it is stressing me out. What if people don't like it? What if I can't fit my writing within the word count, etc? As you can already tell, I am someone who finds it easy to create stress or fall foul of it in all situations.

I now realise that stress has always been a part of my life, even as a child. I care deeply about people – I always have – and also worry desperately what they think of me. A top notch people pleaser, if someone else was happy because of something that I'd done, I was relieved of stress. For a short while at least.

I put enormous pressure on myself to succeed at university and ended up with glandular fever and depression in my second year, so stressed by the pressures that I had to take a year out. I did graduate finally, but stress was a huge part of my daily life there.

That was ten years ago. Since then, I have chosen jobs and a career pathway which have, by coincidence, been extremely challenging and stressful. For me, each day started before I woke. I dreamed about the day ahead: in my first job as a teacher, I dreamed I was planning a lesson for year eight: how would I cope with the screaming and special educational needs whilst trying to teach *Romeo and Juliet*?

Now, as a business advisor, I regularly have dreams about spreadsheets: how to collate the data to convey the information I'm working on effectively? How I should present myself in order to be accepted as a member of the team?

At one previous employer, I suffered such severe stress from the lack of support I received from my manager that I decided to leave. The aftermath was a serious episode of stress-related depression, which was debilitating, distressing and led me to address the stress that has been the common thread through my life.

I'm now becoming more honest about stress at work and being braver in my self-belief that I am not necessarily at fault for this situation. This is tough because we exist in uncertain times, with few jobs for people at any level, and I worry being honest about my stress puts my career progression at risk.

However, I'm now getting better at telling myself that my health is more important. Also, why would I want to continue working in a way that makes me more stressed than ever because of the pressures I put on myself to achieve what may be impossible? I take breaks from work every hour if I can, just for a few minutes. I take my lunch and get out of the office and I feel that I have a right to do this because it makes me more productive.

I have learned about mindfulness (a practice of focusing on the present moment, while acknowledging and accepting my feelings, thoughts and sensations at a given time). I was diabolically bad at this at first. I just don't sit still and I definitely don't focus on one thing at a time. There is too much to be done!

However, I now realise that I need to find a way of coping with the hundreds of thoughts that enter my head and find at least a few minutes every day to put them aside and try to relax. Headspace, incidentally, is a great app for this – I've even used it on crowded commuter trains and managed to stay calm on the way to work, so it really is effective!

Finally and simply, I have begun the daily practice of deep breathing. I take four slow breaths in and then try to exhale over six to eight counts, using my diaphragm to breathe deeply into my body and focus my mind on this exercise. As stress turned to acute anxiety this year, the deep breathing has been a tremendous help to shift my focus away from the root of the anxiety and has gone at least some way, every time, to calming me down and enabling me to carry on through the day.

Stress is a really difficult issue, especially in the busy, competitive world that we live in. But by being more honest with myself about the stress in my life, I now feel calmer, more in control at work and in my life. And this makes me more productive and happier too!

5 November 2014

⇨ The above information is reprinted with kind permission from Mind. Please visit www.mind.org.uk for further information.

© Mind 2015

How colouring books are helping adults beat stress and anxiety

By Rachel Moss

Colouring books for adults are outselling cookery books in France, and now they appear to be taking over bookshelves in the UK, too. But why?

While drawing between the lines was once reserved for children, colouring is now being used as a form of alternative therapy to help adults relieve stress and anxiety.

According to the Mental Health Foundation, 59% of adults in Britain say they are more stressed today than they were five years ago. It's no wonder we're looking for a way to feel calm.

But is grabbing the crayons the answer?

'Colouring is a great way to introduce yourself to the concept of mindfulness,' Tiddy Rowan, author of *The Little Book Of Mindfulness* and *Colour Yourself Calm* tells HuffPost UK Lifestyle.

'One gets so engrossed in colouring, it's an extraordinary activity - in fact, if you watch children playing with crayons you can see just how absorbing it is.'

Tiddy believes colouring can make mindfulness more accessible to stressed adults as the action requires the mind to focus on the present moment.

'Sometimes when you're trying to remember a fact but you can't think of the answer, it will only come to you later when you're doing something else entirely. Colouring can help us to experience clarity of the mind more easily,' she adds.

Co-illustrator of *The Creative Therapy Colouring Book* Richard Merritt agrees that colouring can provide a much needed distraction from stress, and says the experience can transport us back to easier, childhood days.

'When you're colouring, you're not really thinking about anything else. In that moment - when you're sitting down with a traditional piece of paper and some pens, no apps, no noise - you almost go back to being a kid again. Colouring provides a bit of escapism.

'If you put a piece of paper and a crayon in front of a child, they'll start drawing, but I think as an adult you lose that spontaneity,' he says.

Facebook groups have been set up in response to the colouring book trend, with women (the gender predominantly taking part in the activity) coming together and sharing their stories online.

Cynthia Riviere, who administrates a Facebook group of more than 1,000 colouring book fans, spends more than an hour a day filling in the gaps of her favourite books.

She told *The Telegraph*: 'I realised that colouring makes my headaches go away. I concentrate, my breathing slows down and I move into a deep calm.'

This sense of calm that Cynthia and may others experience when colouring may be down to the simplicity of the activity. Recent studies have shown that the majority of adults feel like they are constantly looking at a screen, and crave a slower pace life.

Both Richard and Tiddy believe the growing interest in mindfulness and alternative therapy stems from our dissatisfaction with modern culture.

'We are constantly bombarded with technology, you can download apps to your phone in a few seconds and it's too much for us to take in. Colouring allows us to go back to a slower pace and I think people appreciate that,' Richard says.

According to Tiddy, colouring can help us to reconnect with ourselves which in turn can help us reach out to those around us.

'We're reaching out to each other on social media, but that isn't satisfying. We connect to others through a screen today, but mindfulness encourages us to live in the present moment and connect to those physically around us.

By making a few simple lifestyle changes, mindfulness is something you can begin to practice immediately - it doesn't require extensive study, expensive classes or a big time commitment.

'The interesting thing about mindfulness is that it's got no allegiance to any spiritual or religious beliefs, it's about the self,' Tiddy says. 'I think that's perhaps key to the popularity of these colouring books.'

7 October 2014

⇨ The above information is reprinted with kind permission from The Huffington Post UK. Please visit www.huffingtonpost.co.uk for further information.

Attitudes to
Counselling & Psychotherapy

Key findings of our 2014 Survey

bacp
British Association for
Counselling & Psychotherapy

Background

Our latest survey explores the British public's attitudes to counselling and psychotherapy, and highlights changes in attitudes since our previous surveys in 2004 and 2010.

2084 adults from across the UK completed this survey, which was conducted by Ipsos MORI in March 2014.

Have you ever consulted a counsellor or psychotherapist?

Total respondents
UP **7%**
28% 2014
21% 2010

Gender split
32%
23%

Age groups
55–75 yrs old	24%
45–54 yrs old	32%
35–44 yrs	38%
25–34 yrs old	26%
16–24 yrs old	18%

54% of people say that a family member, friend, work colleague or themselves **have consulted a counsellor or psychotherapist**
54%

Seeking help

Percentage of people who said they'd know where to seek help if they had, or experienced:

WORKPLACE STRESS	**45%**
GAMBLING ADDICTION	**52%**
ANXIETY	**61%**
DEPRESSION	**71%**

People would seek help from a variety of different sources:

64% GP
41% Counsellor or psychotherapist
44% Consult a family member
30% Telephone helpline

27% Contact an advice agency/charity
39% Look online
47% Self-help books or pamphlets

76% of people say they'd prefer to speak to a counsellor face to face, with only **9%** saying they'd prefer to speak online

76%
9%
14% SELF-HARM PORNOGRAPHY SEX ADDICTION
? **73%**

That said, with regards to problems relating to self-harm, pornography or sex addiction, **14%** of people say they'd rather speak online. **73%** of these said they'd prefer to speak online as it would make them feel more anonymous

Acceptance

In 2004, **60%** of people agreed that "people today spend too much time dwelling on their emotional difficulties," in 2014 this has dropped to **39%**

60% 2004
39% 2014

64% of people think that counselling should be available to all school children in schools
64%

69% of people think that the world would be a better place if people talked about their feelings more
69%

Workplace & coaching

48% of people say they feel stressed more regularly these days than they did five years ago
STRESS **48%**

32% of people say their job causes them more stress than anything else in their life.

In London this figure is higher, with **37%** saying their job causes them the most stress
32%
37%

Have you ever taken part in a coaching session?
YES 16%
♂ **18%** ♀ **14%**

53% YES
53% of people say they would accept a free coaching session offered by their employer

37% of people would be more likely to accept the offer of coaching by an employer than counselling, compared to **17%** who would chose counselling over coaching

37% COACHING
17% COUNSELLING

About BACP

BACP is a professional body and a registered charity that sets standards for therapeutic practice and provides information for therapists, clients of therapy, and the public.

We have over 40,000 members, working within a range of settings, including the NHS, schools and universities, workplaces and private practice, as well as third sector environments including voluntary, community and pastoral settings.

BACP Media

We are committed to providing prompt responses to media enquiries, drawing on our extensive member network of experts and spokespeople.

For all media enquiries, call our media team on 01455 883342, or email media@bacp.co.uk.

bacp
British Association for
Counselling & Psychotherapy

Company limited by guarantee 2175320
Registered in England & Wales.
Registered Charity 298361

Version 1

Stress at work

Tips to reduce and manage job and workplace stress.

While some workplace stress is normal, excessive stress can interfere with your productivity and impact your physical and emotional health. And your ability to deal with it can mean the difference between success or failure.

You can't control everything in your work environment, but that doesn't mean you're powerless – even when you're stuck in a difficult situation. Finding ways to manage workplace stress isn't about making huge changes or rethinking career ambitions, but rather about focusing on the one thing that's always within your control: you.

Coping with work stress in today's uncertain climate

For workers everywhere, the troubled economy may feel like an emotional roller coaster. 'Layoffs' and 'budget cuts' have become bywords in the workplace, and the result is increased fear, uncertainty, and higher levels of stress. Since job and workplace stress increase in times of economic crisis, it's important to learn new and better ways of coping with the pressure.

Your emotions are contagious, and stress has an impact on the quality of your interactions with others. The better you are at managing your own stress, the more you'll positively affect those around you, and the less other people's stress will negatively affect you.

You can learn how to manage job stress

There are a variety of steps you can take to reduce both your overall stress levels and the stress you find on the job and in the workplace. These include:

⇨ Taking responsibility for improving your physical and emotional well being.

⇨ Avoiding pitfalls by identifying knee jerk habits and negative attitudes that add to the stress you experience at work.

⇨ Learning better communication skills to ease and improve your relationships with management and coworkers.

Tip 1: Recognise warning signs of excessive stress at work

When you feel overwhelmed at work, you lose confidence and may become irritable or withdrawn. This can make you less productive and less effective in your job, and make the work seem less rewarding. If you ignore the warning signs of work stress, they can lead to bigger problems. Beyond interfering with job performance and satisfaction, chronic or intense stress can also lead to physical and emotional health problems.

Tip 2: Reduce job stress by taking care of yourself

When stress at work interferes with your ability to perform in your job, manage your personal life, or adversely impacts your health, it's time to take action. Start by paying attention to your physical and emotional health. When your own needs are taken care of, you're stronger and more resilient to stress. The better you feel, the better equipped you'll be to manage work stress without becoming overwhelmed.

Taking care of yourself doesn't require a total lifestyle overhaul. Even small things can lift your mood, increase your energy, and make you feel like you're back in the driver's seat. Take things one step at a time, and as you make more positive lifestyle choices, you'll soon notice a reduction in your stress levels, both at home and at work.

Get moving

Regular exercise is a powerful stress reliever – even though it may be the last thing you feel like doing. Aerobic exercise – activity that raises your heart rate and makes you sweat – is a hugely effective way to lift your mood, increase energy, sharpen focus, and relax both the mind and body. For maximum stress relief, try to get at least 30 minutes of heart-pounding activity on most days. If it's easier to fit into your schedule, break up the activity into two or three shorter segments.

Make food choices that keep you going

Low blood sugar can make you feel anxious and irritable, while eating too much can make you lethargic. Healthy eating can help you get through stressful work days. By eating small but frequent meals, you can help your body maintain an even level of blood sugar, keep your energy up, stay focused, and avoid mood swings.

Drink alcohol in moderation and avoid nicotine

Alcohol temporarily reduces anxiety and worry, but too much can cause anxiety as it wears off. Drinking to relieve job stress may also eventually lead to alcohol abuse and dependence. Similarly, smoking when you're feeling stressed and overwhelmed may seem calming, but nicotine is a powerful stimulant – leading to higher, not lower, levels of anxiety.

Get enough sleep

Not only can stress and worry can cause insomnia, but a lack of sleep can leave you vulnerable to even more stress. When you're well-rested, it's much easier to keep your emotional balance, a key factor in coping with job and workplace stress. Try to improve the quality of your sleep by keeping a sleep schedule and aiming for eight hours a night.

Get support

Close relationships are vital to helping you through times of stress so reach out to family and friends. Simply sharing your feelings face to face with another person can help relieve some of the stress. The other person doesn't have to try to 'fix' your problems; he or she just has to be a good listener. Accepting support is not a sign of weakness and it won't mean you're a burden to others. In fact, most friends will be flattered that you trust them enough to confide in them, and it will only strengthen your bond.

Tip 3: Reduce job stress by prioritising and organising

When job and workplace stress threatens to overwhelm you, there are simple steps you can take to regain control over yourself and the situation. Your new-found ability to maintain a sense of self-control in stressful situations will often be well-received by coworkers, managers, and subordinates alike, which can lead to better relationships at work. Here are some suggestions for reducing job stress by prioritising and organising your responsibilities.

Time management tips for reducing job stress

Create a balanced schedule. Analyse your schedule, responsibilities and daily tasks. All work and no play is a recipe for burnout. Try to find a balance between work and family life, social activities and solitary pursuits, daily responsibilities and downtime.

Don't over-commit yourself. Avoid scheduling things back-to-back or trying to fit too much into one day. All too often, we underestimate how long things will take. If you've got too much on your plate, distinguish between the 'shoulds' and the 'musts.' Drop tasks that aren't truly necessary to the bottom of the list or eliminate them entirely.

Try to leave earlier in the morning. Even ten to 15 minutes can make the difference between frantically rushing to your desk and having time to ease into your day. Don't add to your stress levels by running late.

Plan regular breaks. Make sure to take short breaks throughout the day to take a walk or sit back and clear your mind. Also try to get away from your desk or workstation for lunch. Stepping away from work to briefly relax and recharge will help you be more, not less, productive.

Task management tips for reducing job stress

Prioritise tasks. Make a list of tasks you have to do, and tackle them in order of importance. Do the high-priority items first. If you have something particularly unpleasant to do, get it

over with early. The rest of your day will be more pleasant as a result.

Break projects into small steps. If a large project seems overwhelming, make a step-by-step plan. Focus on one manageable step at a time, rather than taking on everything at once.

Delegate responsibility. You don't have to do it all yourself. If other people can take care of the task, why not let them? Let go of the desire to control or oversee every little step. You'll be letting go of unnecessary stress in the process.

Be willing to compromise. When you ask someone to contribute differently to a task, revise a deadline, or change their behaviour at work, be willing to do the same. Sometimes, if you can both bend a little, you'll be able to find a happy middle ground that reduces the stress levels for everyone.

Tip 4: Reduce job stress by improving emotional intelligence

Even if you're in a job where the environment has grown increasingly stressful, you can retain a large measure of self-control and self-confidence by understanding and practicing emotional intelligence. Emotional intelligence is the ability to manage and use your emotions in positive and constructive ways. When it comes to satisfaction and success at work, emotional intelligence matters just as much as intellectual ability. Emotional intelligence is about communicating with others in ways that draw people to you, overcome differences, repair wounded feelings, and defuse tension and stress.

Emotional intelligence in the workplace

Emotional intelligence in the workplace has four major components:

⇨ Self-awareness – The ability to recognize your emotions and their impact while using gut feelings to guide your decisions.

⇨ Self-management – The ability to control your emotions and behaviour and adapt to changing circumstances.

⇨ Social awareness – The ability to sense, understand, and react

to other's emotions and feel comfortable socially.

⇨ Relationship management – The ability to inspire, influence and connect to others and manage conflict.

The five key skills of emotional intelligence

There are five key skills that you need to master in order to raise your emotional intelligence and manage stress at work.

⇨ Realise when you're stressed, recognise your particular stress response, and become familiar with sensual cues that can rapidly calm and energise you. The best way to reduce stress quickly is through the senses: through sight, sound, smell, taste and touch. But each person responds differently to sensory input, so you need to find things that are soothing to you.

⇨ Stay connected to your internal emotional experience so you can appropriately manage your own emotions. Your moment-to-moment emotions influence your thoughts and actions, so pay attention to your feelings and factor them into your decision making at work. If you ignore your emotions you won't be able to fully understand your own motivations and needs, or to communicate effectively with others.

⇨ Recognise and effectively use nonverbal cues and body language. In many cases, what we say is less important than how we say it or the other nonverbal signals we send out, such as eye contact, facial expression, tone of voice, posture, gesture and touch. Your nonverbal messages can either produce a sense of interest, trust and desire for connection – or they can generate confusion, distrust, and stress. You also need to be able to accurately read and respond to the nonverbal cues that other people send you at work.

⇨ Develop the capacity to meet challenges with humour. There is no better stress buster than a hearty laugh and nothing reduces stress quicker in the workplace than mutually shared humour. But, if the laugh is at someone else's expense, you may end up with more rather than less stress.

⇨ Resolve conflict positively. Resolving conflict in healthy, constructive ways can strengthen trust between people and relieve workplace stress and tension. When handling emotionally-charged situations, stay focused in the present by disregarding old hurts and resentments, connect with your emotions, and hear both the words and the nonverbal cues being used. If a conflict can't be resolved, choose to end the argument, even if you still disagree.

Tip 5: Reduce job stress by breaking bad habits

Many of us make job stress worse with negative thoughts and behaviour. If you can turn around these self-defeating habits, you'll find employer-imposed stress easier to handle.

⇨ Resist perfectionism. No project, situation or decision is ever perfect, so trying to attain perfection on everything will simply add unnecessary stress to your day. When you set unrealistic goals for yourself or try to do too much, you're setting yourself up to fall short. Aim to do your best, no one can ask for more than that.

⇨ Clean up your act. If you're always running late, set your clocks and

watches fast and give yourself extra time. If your desk is a mess, file and throw away the clutter; just knowing where everything is saves time and cuts stress. Make to-do lists and cross off items as you accomplish them. Plan your day and stick to the schedule – you'll feel less overwhelmed.

⇨ Flip your negative thinking. If you see the downside of every situation and interaction, you'll find yourself drained of energy and motivation. Try to think positively about your work, avoid negative-thinking co-workers, and pat yourself on the back about small accomplishments, even if no one else does.

⇨ Don't try to control the uncontrollable. Many things at work are beyond our control – particularly the behaviour of other people. Rather than stressing out over them, focus on the things you can control such as the way you choose to react to problems.

Tip 6: Learn how managers or employers can reduce job stress

It's in a manager's best interest to keep stress levels in the workplace to a minimum. Managers can act as positive role models, especially in times of high stress, by following the tips outlined in this article. If a respected manager can remain calm in stressful work situations, it is much easier for his or her employees to also remain calm.

Additionally, there are a number of organisational changes that managers and employers can make to reduce workplace stress. These include:

Improve communication

⇨ Share information with employees to reduce uncertainty about their jobs and futures.

⇨ Clearly define employees' roles and responsibilities.

⇨ Make communication friendly and efficient, not mean-spirited or petty.

Consult your employees

⇨ Give workers opportunities to participate in decisions that affect their jobs.

⇨ Consult employees about scheduling and work rules.

⇨ Be sure the workload is suitable to employees' abilities and resources; avoid unrealistic deadlines.

⇨ Show that individual workers are valued.

⇨ Offer rewards and incentives.

⇨ Praise good work performance, both verbally and officially, through schemes such as Employee of the Month.

⇨ Provide opportunities for career development.

⇨ Promote an 'entrepreneurial' work climate that gives employees more control over their work.

Cultivate a friendly social climate

⇨ Provide opportunities for social interaction among employees.

⇨ Establish a zero-tolerance policy for harassment.

⇨ Make management actions consistent with organisational values.

⇨ The above information is reprinted with kind permission from Helpguide.org. Please visit www.helpguide.org for further information.

THAT'S THE WAY IT USED TO BE!

Ten stress busters

What's making you stressed?

If you're stressed, whether by your job or by something more personal, the first step to feeling better is to identify the cause.

The most unhelpful thing you can do is turn to something unhealthy to help you cope, such as smoking or drinking.

'In life, there's always a solution to a problem,' says Professor Cary Cooper, an occupational health expert at the University of Lancaster. 'Not taking control of the situation and doing nothing will only make your problems worse.'

He says the keys to good stress management are building emotional strength, being in control of your situation, having a good social network and adopting a positive outlook.

What you can do to address stress

These are Professor Cooper's top ten stress-busting suggestions:

Be active

If you have a stress-related problem, physical activity can get you in the right state of mind to be able to identify the causes of your stress and find a solution. 'To deal with stress effectively, you need to feel robust and you need to feel strong mentally. Exercise does that,' says Cooper.

Exercise won't make your stress disappear, but it will reduce some of the emotional intensity that you're feeling, clearing your thoughts and enabling you to deal with your problems more calmly.

Take control

There's a solution to any problem. 'If you remain passive, thinking, 'I can't do anything about my problem', your stress will get worse,' says Professor Cooper. 'That feeling of loss of control is one of the main causes of stress and lack of wellbeing.'

The act of taking control is in itself empowering, and it's a crucial part of finding a solution that satisfies you and not someone else. Read tips about how to manage your time.

Connect with people

A problem shared is a problem halved. A good support network of colleagues, friends and family can ease your work troubles and help you see things in a different way.

'If you don't connect with people, you won't have support to turn to when you need help,' says Professor Cooper. The activities we do with friends help us relax and we often have a good laugh with them, which is an excellent stress reliever.

'Talking things through with a friend will also help you find solutions to your problems,' says Professor Cooper.

Have some 'me time'

The UK workforce works the longest hours in Europe. The extra hours in the workplace mean that people aren't spending enough time doing things that they really enjoy. 'We all need to take some time for socialising, relaxation or exercise,' says Professor Cooper.

He recommends setting aside a couple of nights a week for some quality 'me time' away from work. 'By earmarking those two days, it means you won't be tempted to work overtime on those days,' he says.

Challenge yourself

Setting yourself goals and challenges, whether at work or outside, such as learning a new language or a new sport, helps to build confidence. That in turn will help you deal with stress.

'By constantly challenging yourself you're being proactive and taking charge of your life,' says Professor Cooper. 'By continuing to learn, you become more emotionally resilient as a person. It arms you with knowledge and makes you

want to do things rather than be passive, such as watching TV all the time.'

Avoid unhealthy habits

Don't rely on alcohol, smoking and caffeine as your ways of coping. 'Men more than women are likely to do this. We call this avoidance behaviour,' says Professor Cooper. 'Women are better at seeking support from their social circle.'

Over the long term, these crutches won't solve your problems. They'll just create new ones. 'It's like putting your head in the sand,' says Professor Cooper. 'It might provide temporary relief but it won't make the problems disappear. You need to tackle the cause of your stress.'

Help other people

Cooper says evidence shows that people who help others, through activities such as volunteering or community work, become more resilient. 'Helping people who are often in situations worse than yours will help you put your problems into perspective,' says Professor Cooper. 'The more you give, the more resilient and happy you feel.'

If you don't have time to volunteer, try to do someone a favour every day. It can be something as small as helping someone to cross the road or going on a coffee run for colleagues. Favours cost nothing to do, and you'll feel better.

Work smarter, not harder

Good time management means quality work rather than quantity. Our long-hours culture is a well-known cause of workplace illness. 'You have to get a work-life balance that suits you,' says Professor Cooper.

Working smarter means prioritising your work, concentrating on the tasks that will make a real difference to your work. 'Leave the least important tasks to last,' says Cooper. 'Accept that your in-tray will always be full. Don't expect it to be empty at the end of the day.'

Be positive

Look for the positives in life, and things for which you're grateful. Write down three things at the end of every day which went well or for which you're grateful.

'People don't always appreciate what they have,' says Professor Cooper. 'Try to be glass half full instead of glass half empty,' he says.

This requires a shift in perspective for those who are more naturally pessimistic.

'It can be done,' he says. 'By making a conscious effort you can train yourself to be more positive about life. Problems are often a question of perspective. If you change your perspective, you may see your situation from a more positive point of view.'

Accept the things you can't change

Changing a difficult situation isn't always possible. If this proves to be the case, recognise and accept things as they are and concentrate on everything that you do have control over.

'If your company is going under and is making redundancies, there's nothing you can do about it,' says Professor Cooper. 'There's no point fighting it. In such a situation, you need to focus on the things that you can control, such as looking for a new job.'

6 January 2014

⇨ The above information is reprinted with kind permission from NHS Choices. Please visit www.nhs.uk for further information.

Why is it important to breathe properly to help anxiety?

We are going to look at hyperventilating (or over-breathing) because when we are anxious we will be over-breathing. Sometimes that has developed into a bad habit which we can be doing all the time without being aware of.

About 60% of panic attacks are accompanied by hyperventilation and many people suffering from anxiety over-breathe even when they think they are relaxed.

The most important thing to understand about hyperventilation or over breathing is that although we can feel as if we haven't enough oxygen in our body, actually the opposite is true.

With hyperventilation the body has too much oxygen. To use this oxygen your body needs a certain amount of carbon dioxide.

When we hyperventilate we do not give the body long enough to retain carbon dioxide and so the body cannot use the oxygen it has. This gives a feeling that there isn't enough air in the body, when actually there is too much. Then we are in the cycle of a chemical imbalance which can cause a lot of nasty symptoms. The problem is the shortage of carbon dioxide that causes many problems. Even though carbon dioxide is a waste gas we do need it in certain parts of the body, especially the brain. Although this chemical imbalance can be extremely unpleasant it will not harm anyone and the breathing technique will help restore the correct balance and give a person control over anxiety.

Control centre

We have a control centre at the base of our brain which measures the levels of carbon dioxide in the blood and decides what to do to keep our breathing balanced. It sends a message to our body on how we should breathe. When we are breathing wrong because the carbon dioxide get low, it goes down a notch and when we start to breathe normally it goes back to its original position. However

if we continue to breathe wrong it stays where it is and encourages us to breathe faster and that is where our breathing can become a bad habit and we are unaware that this is the cause of some of our symptoms. If anxiety and stress become a bad habit the body becomes sensitised and is triggered more easily to panic. Regular relaxation and correct breathing will stop the production of stress hormones (cortisol, non-adrenalin and adrenalin)

Symptoms that may be experienced

Light headedness, giddiness, dizziness, shortness of breath, heart palpitation, numbness, chest pains, dry mouth, clammy hands, difficulty in swallowing, sweating, weakness, fatigue.

It takes a lot more energy when we are breathing wrong so that can help us to feel very tired.

If you find that your breathing pattern is irregular or uncomfortable a lot of the time, the best way to reset it is by exercising. Start of gradually and check with your doctor if you are not used to exercise.

Bad breathing restricts blood flow to the brain, which affects nerve cells, which are the first to respond. This can cause dizziness and tingling. Low carbon dioxide levels affect the nervous system. This puts the body on alert. Continued bad breathing causes exhaustion, tiredness and depression. Oxygen levels are lower in the brain and this means we cannot concentrate and can feel not real and cut off. The drop in oxygen levels stimulates the breathing control centre which then increases the breathing rate to compensate and this then encourages hyperventilation. The brain resets and an over-breathing habit may be formed. We may not even be aware of what has happened.

Practising the breathing technique will stimulate the part of the nervous system responsible for relaxation and calming the body down. This is a basic law of biology and if you breathe this way the body will have no choice but to relax.

It may take a few minutes but the body will respond regardless of what the mind is thinking. Doing this regularly with the relaxation CD will cause general anxiety to come down. With practice regularly we want to try and aim for keeping anxiety at a lower base line of arousal that everyone has. Then it stops the body being anxious at the slightest thing and it becomes harder to get stressed.

Regular relaxation and the breathing technique start to stop the production of stress hormones in the body so it becomes harder to panic.

Try this test

Let us try together and see where you are breathing from, the chest or the tummy. Put one hand below your collar bone and one on your diaphragm, which is just below your rib cage and tummy button. Then breathe how you normally would breathe. Are you breathing from the chest are or you breathing correctly from your diaphragm?

Take a deep breath through the mouth and see how that feels. Can you feel cold air hitting the back of the throat? That in fact will make us breathe quicker, which will increase anxiety and the symptoms we experience.

Now breathe through the nose with the mouth shut. How does that feel? The air is warm and also filtered of germs so is much healthier.

Diaphragm

The diaphragm is like a sheet of muscle and is shaped like an umbrella and goes up and down as we breathe. It flattens down to expand the lungs and that is why the stomach expands as we breathe in. It draws in oxygen-rich air with little effort. As the diaphragm relaxes the dome shape is restored and carbon dioxide-rich air is gently exhaled.

The diaphragm is tailor made to fit your body and its sole purpose is to supply the right amount of air to the lungs during rest and normal activity. Have you ever looked at babies when they are breathing? You can hardly see their body moving and that is because they are breathing from the diaphragm. If you have pets, if we watch cats and dogs for example, they just flop, drop and again breathe very steady and rhythmic. This is a perfect example of breathing from the diaphragm. If you place one hand gently on your tummy, just below your rib cage and belly button and as you breathe in push your tummy gently up and as you breathe out your tummy should gently come down again. We are not going to be deep breathing but breathing very rhythmic and steady. No pause between the in and out breaths. Try and just concentrate on your breath going in and out. We should try and aim for 8 to 10 breathes a minute. Breathing in and out counts as one breath.

We breathe in through the nose with the mouth closed to four in and breathe out again to four through the nose, keeping the mouth closed. Feel the stomach expand as you breathe in, inflate it like a balloon and as you breathe out allow your stomach to deflate. Try and just concentrate on your breath going in and out. We should try and aim for eight to ten breathes a minute. Breathing in and out counts as one breath.

What this does is restore the chemical imbalance and it will calm the mind and body down, which will reduce the symptoms.

The best way to start is lying on the bed and place your hands gently on your stomach (where the diaphragm is) with your finger tips touching and as you breathe in the finger tips should come apart and as you breathe out they come back together again. As you get used to doing the breathing technique do practise your breathing sitting in a chair, then perhaps when washing up, or standing in a queue in the supermarket, so eventually you can learn to do this way of breathing anywhere in your anxious situations. You do have to practise it regularly because your body is probably not used to breathing this way and needs time to adjust because it is something new.

Problems

Resist the temptation to take huge gulps of air in. If we breathe in big we are going to breathe out big too, further depleting carbon dioxide levels.

If a person feels dizzy it means they are still big breathing rather than deep breathing. To overcome this cup both hands over the mouth and nose and re breathe carbon dioxide-rich air for five of six breathes, then rest. Repeat this until the dizziness has gone.

We may have the urge to yawn, sigh or gulp in air. It may seem overwhelming and very uncomfortable but this is a sign of progress and shows that the breathing is beginning to work. The body is trying to make you breathe faster but with practice the breathing centre will adjust and your body will get used to the new way of breathing.

The diaphragm may struggle at first, especially if it has been out of action for a while. Like any other group of muscles that have not been used, the diaphragm may need strengthening.

Be patient, it will work better the more you practice.

Set the alarm five minutes earlier in the morning and start the day with good breathing practice. Check the chest area regularly through the day, correct the breathing and forget it. It is important not to worry about the breathing and let it come naturally. As you become accustomed to the breathing there will be less need to check the chest. During stressful times, however, it pays to check the breathing rate and patterns.

Concentrating on the breathing helps bring down and calm anxiety

4 August 2014

⇨ The above information is reprinted with kind permission from No Panic. Please visit www.nopanic.org.uk for further information.

Treating post-traumatic stress disorder: confronting the horror

THE CONVERSATION

An article from The Conversation.

By Mark Creamer, Professorial Fellow, Department of Psychiatry at University of Melbourne

While human beings have always known about the mental health effects of trauma, it was only in 1980 that the term post-traumatic stress disorder, or PTSD, was coined. This acceptance spawned an explosion of research on the causes, vulnerabilities, and optimum treatments for PTSD.

We have since learnt a great deal about how to help people with this disabling and often chronic condition. Evidence-based treatment guidelines in Australia and the United Kingdom are consistent in their recommendation of 'trauma-focused psychological treatment' as the first line approach for PTSD. Of these approaches, the strongest body of evidence supports an intervention known as 'prolonged exposure'.

PTSD is a complex disorder, with multiple symptom groups. Avoidance of trauma reminders, persistent hyper-arousal (constantly looking out for potential danger), and negative mood are key features. The hallmark, however, is that of 're-experiencing the trauma' in the form of intrusive images, memories and nightmares.

It is this inability to move on – being constantly haunted by the past horror – that drives the other symptom clusters. Any successful treatment, therefore, must target these traumatic memories and prolonged exposure is designed specifically to do that.

Prolonged exposure is a common-sense approach. We are all familiar with 'getting back on the horse' – confronting what frightens us and not avoiding it. The most successful treatments for all anxiety disorders are built around this concept.

To treat someone who is very frightened of spiders, for example, we would help them to face their fear.

Starting with a small spider in a jar across the room, we would gradually get closer and gradually move to bigger spiders. At each step the anxiety would increase but, by staying with it and not running away, it gradually reduces or 'habituates' so that we can move on to the next step.

Treating PTSD is essentially the same process. We help the person to gradually confront situations, places and activities they've avoided since the traumatic event because they cause great anxiety; we call this *in vivo* (or live) exposure. In PTSD, however, the main 'feared object' is not outside the person, it is the memory of their traumatic experience.

People with PTSD – consciously or unconsciously – block out and avoid these painful memories. Prolonged exposure helps them to gradually confront the memories and 'work through' the experience in a safe and controlled manner; we call this imaginal exposure. Each time they confront the memory without avoiding, and stay with it long enough for the distress to reduce, they make another step towards recovery.

The first component of prolonged exposure is to explain clearly what we are doing and why; after all, we are asking them to do what they fear most. We explain the rationale and process in detail, often using metaphors to illustrate the mechanisms involved.

We also teach them strategies to manage distress. These are not to be used during prolonged exposure, but it is important for people to feel confident about controlling their distress at other times.

We then ask the person to talk through the event. Just as we graded our exposure for the spider phobic, we try to do for the memory. On the first few runs through, the person might talk with their eyes open, in the past tense

('I walked into the park…'), and skip over the worst aspects.

On later exposures, however, it is important to confront all aspects of the experience, to ensure there are no 'skeletons in the closet' that will cause problems later. So we use eyes closed, present tense ('I am walking into the park…'), focusing on all senses (sights, sounds, smells, tastes, touch), and – as treatment progresses – confronting the worst aspects of the experience in detail.

We monitor the patent's distress regularly to ensure it is reducing before moving on to the next level.

Imaginal prolonged exposure is a powerful process for both therapist and client. It results both in reduced distress and in greater understanding of what happened and why. 'Putting the pieces of the jigsaw puzzle together' is crucial to recovery and has long been recognised as an effective treatment.

Early variations on prolonged exposure (such as 'abreaction') used drugs to access the memories, while more recent approaches (such as desensitisation) placed a heavy emphasis on relaxation and arousal reduction during exposure. We now know that neither is recommended; people can access the memories, and can tolerate the distress, without these additions.

While there is a common perception that the best way to recover from trauma is to forget about it and focus on the future, the research and clinical evidence is clear: for trauma survivors with PTSD, that is not the case. Indeed, the evidence is now sufficiently strong that it would be negligent not to offer a trauma-focused psychological treatment to a patient with PTSD.

13 July 2014

⇨ The above information is reprinted with kind permission from The Conversation. Please visit www.theconversation.com for further information.

'I had three or four flashbacks a day'

In some exceptional cases, the vivid recollection of a trauma can cause distress many years after the incident. Andy, an ex-fire officer, describes his experience of post-traumatic stress disorder (PTSD) and how the right treatment has helped him to move on.

'The event that caused my trauma happened 20 years ago when I was a fire officer. I was in charge of an appliance at a house fire where three people had died. It was my job to take their remains out of the house.

'A few days later I became distressed and started crying and feeling upset. This strong reaction came as a shock, but I said nothing at the time. I think this was partly because I didn't want to share my emotions with anybody.

'My feelings and thoughts continued to bother me for a few weeks. After a while I decided that, because of my job, being like this was no good and I had to put these emotions to one side.

'These early responses to the trauma indicated the huge wave of feelings and sensations that would come back 17 years later in a way I couldn't ignore.

'I was still a firefighter. I kept remembering that terrible event and the feelings it left me with, but I tried not to think about it. A few days later my colleagues and I were at another house fire. It was similar to the one in which the family had died. Suddenly, I felt as if I wasn't there. My mind was totally occupied in a flashback of the original incident. One of my colleagues had to step in and take over from me.

'From then on I started to become distressed for no real reason. Everything seemed emotional, and I felt raw and exposed. I got easily frustrated, which made me short-tempered and angry.

'When the distress was at its worst, I had three or four flashbacks a day. I would sweat and become very nervous as I remembered the events 20 years ago. All the smells were there, and I even felt the heat of the fire moving across my face. People who saw me say that I sometimes walked about and mouthed words, but I was completely detached from my surroundings.

'That was when it became obvious that I couldn't go on. After some time, I had a course of trauma-focused cognitive behavioural therapy with a PTSD charity called ASSIST. They helped me to understand that I had experienced something abnormal, that none of it was my fault, and that there was nothing wrong or crazy about my emotional responses.

'Talking about the fire was uncomfortable at times, but it helped me to process my memories so that they stopped reappearing as flashbacks. They have gone now, and I am able to get on with my life.'

24 September 2013

⇨ The above information is reprinted with kind permission from NHS Choices. Please visit www.nhs.uk for further information.

Key facts

⇨ The total number of cases of work-related stress, depression or anxiety in 2013/14 was 487,000 (39%) out of a total of 1,241,000 cases for all work-related illnesses. (page 3)

⇨ The total number of working days lost due to stress, depression or anxiety was 11.3 million in 2013/14, an average of 23 days per case of stress, depression or anxiety. (page 3)

⇨ Mental health problems affect one person in every four, making it the leading cause of disability. Its direct cost to England alone is estimated at £41.8 billion per annum but the wider costs in terms of the economy, benefits, lost productivity at work, amounts to more than £70 billion per year. (page 9)

⇨ A nationally representative sample of 1,000 university students found that 75% of them had personally experienced some kind of emotional distress while at university. Stress topped the list at 65% whilst 43% of students stated that they had experienced anxiety, loneliness and feelings of not being able to cope. Around one third of students had felt depressed or homesick at some time whilst 29% had worried about not fitting in at university. (page 12)

⇨ 95 per cent of imprisoned young offenders have a mental health disorder. (page 14)

⇨ Only one in 20 people never feel anxious. (page 17)

⇨ Younger people are much more likely to feel anxious about relationships. (page 17)

⇨ Four in every ten employed people experience anxiety about their work. (page 17)

⇨ About one in 20 people have an anxiety disorder at any one time. (page 18)

⇨ In the 12 months to November 2013 almost three out of ten anxiety admissions were women aged 60 and over (2,440 out of 8,720, or 28 per cent), with 65 to 69 the most common age group of female patient admissions (437, or eight per cent of all female admissions). The most common age group for male patient admissions was 45 to 49 (279, or 8.5 per cent of all male admissions). (page 21)

⇨ Around 1.9% of British adults experience a phobia of some description, and women are twice as likely to be affected by this problem as men. (page 22)

⇨ Post-Traumatic Stress Disorder (PTSD) affects 2.6% of men and 3.3% of women. (page 22)

⇨ Generalised Anxiety Disorder affects between 2–5% of the population, yet accounts for as much as 30% of the mental health problems seen by GPs. (page 22)

⇨ Comfort eating is used by a quarter of people to cope with feelings of anxiety, and women and young people are more likely to use this as a way of coping. (page 23)

⇨ Fewer than one in ten people have sought help from their GP to deal with anxiety, although those who feel anxious more frequently are much more likely to do this. (page 23)

⇨ Research, which surveyed 2,134 respondents aged 18 and above, found that one in ten respondents have taken more than six days off work due to stress. (page 25)

⇨ In 2013, around 70 million working days were lost because of mental health. (page 26)

⇨ A survey of almost 1,400 workers revealed that almost a third believed work-related stress could lead to high blood pressure, while one in five feared it could cause a heart attack. (page 27)

⇨ A third of people polled said they had put on weight because of work, half ate more unhealthily, a quarter drink more and 43% believe work has caused them to exercise less. (page 27)

⇨ 69% of people think that the world would be a better place if people talked about their feelings more. (page 31)

⇨ 28% of people have consulted a counsellor or psychotherapist. (page 31)

⇨ 48% of people say they feel stressed more regularly these days than they did five years ago. (page 31)

⇨ 76% of people would prefer to speak to a counsellor face to face, with only 9% saying they'd prefer to speak online. (page 31)

⇨ About 60% of panic attacks are accompanied by hyperventilation and many people suffering from anxiety over-breathe even when they think they are relaxed. (page 36)

Agoraphobia
Fear of public places.

Angst
A feeling of anxiety or apprehension.

Anxiety
Feeling nervous, worried or distressed, sometimes to a point where the person feels so overwhelmed that they find everyday life very difficult to handle.

Cardiovascular disease
Conditions that affect the heart and circulation.

Cognitive behavioural therapy (CBT)
A psychological treatment which assumes that behavioural and emotional reactions are learned over a long period. A cognitive therapist will seek to identify the source of emotional problems and develop techniques to overcome them.

Depression
Someone is said to be significantly depressed, or suffering from depression, when feelings of sadness or misery don't go away quickly and are so bad that they interfere with everyday life. Symptoms can also include low self-esteem and a lack of motivation. Depression can be triggered by a traumatic/difficult event (reactive depression), but not always (e.g. endogenous depression).

Fight or flight response
Also called the stress response, this refers to a physical reaction the body encounters when faced with something it perceives to be a threat. The nervous system is primed, preparing the body to either fight the threat or run away from it. In the past, this response would have helped human beings to survive threats such as predatory animals. While this no longer applies to our modern lifestyles, our bodies will still react with the fight-or-flight response to any perceived threat - an approaching deadline, for example - causing many of the negative symptoms of stress.

Generalised anxiety disorder (GAD)
Someone with GAD has a lot of anxiety (feeling fearful, worried and tense) on most days, and not just in specific situations, and the condition persists long-term. Some of the physical symptoms of anxiety come and go. Someone with this high level of `background anxiety` may also have panic attacks and some phobias.

Mindfulness
Mind-body based training that uses meditation, breathing and yoga techniques to help you focus on your thoughts and feelings. Mindfulness helps you manage your thoughts and feelings better, instead of being overwhelmed by them.

Panic attack
A panic attack is a severe attack of anxiety and fear which occurs suddenly, often without warning, and for no apparent reason. Symptoms can include palpitations, sweating, trembling, nausea and hyperventilation. At least one in ten people have occasional panic attacks. They tend to occur most in young adults.

Phobia
A fear of a situation or thing that is not actually dangerous and which most people do not find troublesome. The nearer a phobic person gets to the situation or thing that makes them anxious, the more anxious they get, and so they tend to avoid it. Away from the thing or situation that makes them feel anxious, they feel fine.

Post-traumatic stress disorder (PTSD)
PTSD is a psychological reaction to a highly traumatic event. It has been known by different names at different times in history: during the First World War, for example, soldiers suffering from PTSD were said to have `shell shock`.

Social anxiety disorder
Fear of social situations.

Stress
Stress is the feeling of being under pressure. A little bit of pressure can be a good thing, helping to motivate you: however, too much pressure or prolonged pressure can lead to stress, which is unhealthy for the mind and body and can cause symptoms such as lack of sleep, loss of appetite and difficulty concentrating.

Work-life balance
The concept of achieving a healthy balance between your career/work commitments and your home-life (family, friends, socialising, leisure activities, etc.).

Assignments

Brainstorming

⇨ In small groups, discuss what you know about stress and anxiety. Consider the following points:

- What is stress?
- What is anxiety?
- How are stress and anxiety different?
- What are some of the causes of stress?
- What are some of the causes of anxiety?
- What kind of things do people do to cope with stress and anxiety?

Research

⇨ Do some research about post-traumatic stress in relation to soldiers in the Army. When did people first start recognising this as a condition? What kind of treatments are available? Write some notes and feedback to your class.

⇨ Look at the graph on page three and conduct a survey amongst your friends, family and classmates asking the same question. Create a graph that displays your results and compare them to the percentages on page three. Are they different or similar? Discuss with a partner.

⇨ Do some research to find out more about the idea of good stress vs. bad stress. Make some notes and discuss your findings with your class.

⇨ Research illegal adoption and write an article or blog post exploring your findings.

Design

⇨ Design a poster that will help people recognise the symptoms of anxiety.

⇨ Choose one of the articles in this book and create an illustration to highlight the key themes/message of your chosen article.

⇨ Design a leaflet that explains stress and anxiety. Try to include some maps and statistics, as well as images or drawings.

⇨ Design a website that will give parents information about anxiety in young people. Think about the kind of information they might need and give your site a name and logo.

⇨ Imagine you work for a charity which campaigns to raise awareness of anxiety amongst young people. Create a name and logo for your company and plan an event that would help highlight your cause and raise money for your charity.

⇨ Create a booklet to help students who are at risk of exam stress. Provide broad information on how to cope with stress, including relaxation techniques, tips on nutrition, advice on how best to prepare for an exam and anything else you think your readers would find helpful – you could even include some stress-busting meal ideas or suggest a relaxation playlist! Keep the tone light and fun and include illustrations.

Oral

⇨ In pairs, role play one of the following situations:

- An employee telling their line manager that they are suffering from work-related stress, and the line manager's response.
- A student telling their friend that they are feeling lonely and anxious, and the friend's advice.

⇨ In small groups, create a three–four minute presentation, aimed at your year group, that explores ways of dealing with stress and anxiety.

⇨ Choose one of the illustrations in this book and, in pairs, discuss what you think the artist was trying to portray with their image.

⇨ As a class, stage a debate in which half of you agree and the other half disagree with the following statement: 'Young people are under too much pressure to perform, which is causing increasing levels of stress and anxiety.'

Reading/writing

⇨ Watch the 2012 film *The Perks of Being a Wallflower* and write a review discussing how the theme of post traumatic stress is explored throughout the film.

⇨ Imagine that you work for a large company where several of your colleagues have recently taken time off due to stress. Write a letter to your line manager, suggesting some changes you think would help to combat stress. You should think carefully about how you could persuade your manager that these are worthwhile changes.

⇨ Write a one-paragraph definition anxiety and then another one-paragraph definition of stress. Compare your definitions.

⇨ Write an article that compares the ways in which men and women experience stress. Use the articles on pages ten and 11 for help, and conduct further research online if you need to.

⇨ Write a blog post from the perspective of a first year University student who is struggling with depression.

Acknowledgements

The publisher is grateful for permission to reproduce the material in this book. While every care has been taken to trace and acknowledge copyright, the publisher tenders its apology for any accidental infringement or where copyright has proved untraceable. The publisher would be pleased to come to a suitable arrangement in any such case with the rightful owner.

Images

All images courtesy of iStock, except page 28 © Craig Garner and page 30 © Morguefile.

Icons on pages 6 and 17 are courtesy of Freepik.

Illustrations

Don Hatcher: pages 7 & 34. Simon Kneebone: pages 4 & 25. Angelo Madrid: pages 12 & 38.

Additional acknowledgements

Editorial on behalf of Independence Educational Publishers by Cara Acred.

With thanks to the Independence team: Mary Chapman, Sandra Dennis, Christina Hughes, Jackie Staines and Jan Sunderland.

Cara Acred

Cambridge

May 2015